AS Geograph for Edexcel

Teacher's Book

Digby ▸ Hurst

OXFORD

Great Clarendon Street, Oxford OX2 6DP

Oxford University Press is a department of the University of Oxford.
It furthers the University's objective of excellence in research,
scholarship, and education by publishing worldwide in

Oxford New York

Auckland Cape Town Dar es Salaam Hong Kong Karachi
Kuala Lumpur Madrid Melbourne Mexico City Nairobi
New Delhi Shanghai Taipei Toronto

With offices in

Argentina Austria Brazil Chile Czech Republic France Greece
Guatemala Hungary Italy Japan Poland Portugal Singapore
South Korea Switzerland Thailand Turkey Ukraine Vietnam

Authors: Bob Digby, Catherine Hurst

British Library Cataloguing in Publication Data

Data available

ISBN 978-0-19-913481-6

10 9 8 7 6 5 4 3 2 1

Printed Bell and Bain Ltd., Glasgow

Paper used in the production of this book is a natural, recyclable product made
from wood grown in sustainable forests. The manufacturing process conforms to
the environmental regulations of the country of origin.

Contents

About this course

This course has been written to meet the requirements of the Edexcel GCE in Geography. It has been written to make AS and A2 learning accessible, and we hope it will help you and your students succeed.

The course components

The students' books
- Two books:
  - AS *Geography for Edexcel*, written to meet the requirements of the Edexcel Advanced Subsidiary GCE in Geography.
  - A2 *Geography for Edexcel*, written to meet the requirements of the Edexcel Advanced GCE in Geography.
- All the content and case studies students will need for their course.
- Coverage of all the core and option topics.
- Chapters divided into clearly-identified units of between two and eight pages.
- Aims of unit given in student-friendly language at the start of each unit.
- 'Over to you' and 'On your own' questions for each unit.
- Exam-style questions for each chapter.
- The first page of each chapter gives the enquiry questions detailed in the specification, and makes it clear to students what they have to know and learn.

The teacher's books
- One for each students' book.
- Material to help you for each unit in the students' books.
- Brief unit overviews.
- Key ideas.
- Unit outcomes.
- Ideas for starters and plenaries.

The Activities and Planning OxBox CD-ROMs
- One for the AS part of the course, one for A2.
- Photographs and resources from the students' books.
- Exam-style questions, with model answers and mark schemes.
- Fieldwork support.
- Answers for 'Over to you' and 'On your own' questions.
- Editable 'Over to you' and 'On your own' questions'.
- Customisable planning materials; the lesson player helps you arrange and launch the resources you want to use in sequence.
- User management facility that allows you to easily import class registers and create user accounts for all your students.

OxBox technology: OxBox CD-ROMs are bought individually. The software then allows the content to be tipped together to create a single resource on your network.

They are customisable – you can add your own resources. There are easy-to-follow guidelines on how to do this.

Using this teacher's book

This teacher's book is intended to save you time and effort. It offers support for the students' book, and will help you prepare detailed course and lesson plans.

What it provides

For each chapter in the students' book, this teacher's book provides:

1 a concise overview of the chapter
2 support for each unit in the chapter

It also has a glossary at the back, covering the terms students will meet.

1 The chapter overview

This is your introduction to the corresponding chapter in the students' book. This is what it provides:

- **Chapter outline**: the title of each unit, together with a one-line summary of what it covers.
- **About the topic**: a brief summary of the topic, set in its specification context.
- **About the chapter**: a brief summary of the content and approach of the students' book chapter.
- **Key vocabulary**: a list of key words and terms for the chapter.

1 The world at risk

Chapter outline

Use this chapter outline and the introductory page of the chapter in the Student Book to give students a mental roadmap for the chapter.

1.1 **What has happened to Tebua?** Tebua's disappearance, and the risks facing some of the world's most remote island nations

1.2 **Hazards and disasters** What hazards and disasters are, and how they affect people

1.3 **Global hazards** How hazards increasingly threaten people's lives and property

1.4 **Hazards and vulnerability** Looking at the idea of vulnerability, and why hazards affect people and places in such different ways

1.5 **Bushfire!** How different strategies reduce some of the impacts of bushfires in Australia

1.6 **Why are some places hazard prone?** Assessing hazard risks in students' own area, using London as an example

1.7 **Hazard hotspots** Multiple hazards in two hazard hotspots: the Philippines and California

1.8 **The causes of climate change** Investigating the causes of climate change and global warming. Natural and long-term, or caused by human activity?

1.9 **The effects of climate change** The effects on Greenland, changing global temperatures, impacts on the world's oceans

1.10 **The impacts of global warming** The impacts on the Arctic and Africa

1.11 **Dealing with climate change – mitigation and adaptation** How mitigation and adaptation strategies can be used to cope with climate change

1.12 **Global warming – which way now?** Options for the future. Has the world already reached 'tipping point'?

1.13 **Strategies for dealing with climate change** How individuals, organisations, governments, and international agreements can help to reduce the impacts of climate change

1.14 **Energy use, efficiency and conservation** Strategies to combat climate change through energy efficiency and conservation

1.15 **Tackling risk and vulnerability in Bangladesh** How Bangladesh can adapt to the increasing risk of flooding caused by global warming

1.16 **Tackling risk and vulnerability in Indonesia** How Indonesia struggles to cope with the increasing risk of natural hazards and other problems

About the topic

This topic has two strands:

1 The risks from hazards
   - There are two main types of hazards – hydrometeorological and geophysical.
   - Hazards can become natural disasters where the population is vulnerable.
   - Hazard hotspots show that the poor lose lives while the rich lose money.

2 Risk and climate change
   - The causes of global warming, relationship to long-term climate change, and impacts.
   - Possible solutions.

About the chapter

- This chapter investigates hazards and disasters, how they increasingly threaten people's lives and property, and the idea of vulnerability.
- It looks at hazard hotspots, with the Philippines and California used as case studies. It investigates causes and effects of climate change and looks at the impacts of global warming on the Arctic and Africa.
- Dealing with climate change, mitigation and adaptation, options for the future, and strategies for dealing with climate change are included.
- The chapter ends with case studies of Bangladesh and Indonesia which explore how these two countries tackle risk and vulnerability.

Key vocabulary

There is no set list of words in the specification that students must know. However, examiners will use some or all of the following words in the examinations, and would expect students to know them and use them in their answers.

adaptation
boreal forest
carbon credits
carbon offsetting
carbon sequestration
carbon sinks
deep sea core samples
destructive boundary
disaster
enhanced greenhouse effect
environmental refugees
exponential
geomorphological
global conveyor belt
greenhouse effect
greenhouse gases
hazard vulnerability
IPCC
lahars
magma chamber
mega-delta

Milankovitch cycles
mitigation
multiple hazards
natural hazard
North Atlantic Drift
permafrost
positive ice-albedo feedback
pyroclastic flows
radiation
saline
scenario
subducted
tectonic
thermohaline circulation
tipping point
tree line
tundra
vent
volcanic emissions
vulnerable populations

The glossary at the end of this book contains many of these words and phrases. For students, the key word boxes in the chapter or the glossary at the end of the Student Book will help them with the meanings of all.

Introduction

2 Support for each unit

These pages give help for each unit in the chapter. This is what they provide:

- **The unit in brief**: tells you what the unit covers, and how it develops.
- **Key ideas**: the key ideas covered in the unit.
- **Unit outcomes**: the expected outcomes for the unit.
- **Ideas for a starter**: several suggestions for a starter.
- **Ideas for plenaries**: several suggestions for plenaries that could be used throughout lessons, not just at the end.

 What has happened to Tebua?

The unit in brief

This 2-page unit acts as an introduction to the topic 'The world at risk' and investigates the risks facing some of the world's most remote island nations. Tebua (one of the islands of Kiribati) in the Pacific Ocean has disappeared – swallowed by rising sea levels. The rest of Kiribati is also suffering from rising sea levels and erosion. People are leaving, becoming the world's first environmental refugees. Rising sea levels are a result of global warming, and along with increases in the number of tropical storms the region suffers from the threat of multiple hazards.

Key ideas

- Rising sea levels are threatening low-lying island nations such as Kiribati in the Pacific.
- People forced to migrate as a result of changes to the environment are called environmental refugees.
- Tebua's disappearance is one sign that global warming is happening.
- Kiribati is in a region at risk from multiple hazards.
- The worst effects of global warming are felt by the poorest countries who make the least contribution to the problem and are least equipped to deal with it.

Unit outcomes

By the end of this unit most students should be able to:
- explain why rising sea levels are threatening nations such as Kiribati;
- define the term environmental refugees;
- suggest why large numbers of environmental refugees could create a political problem in countries such as Australia and New Zealand;
- say how far Kiribati is a nation facing multiple hazards.

Ideas for a starter

1. Show students the photo of Tarawa Atoll on page 6 of the Student Book. Read the first part of the text out loud, i.e. *Early in 2002, writer Curtis A. Moore went in search of Tebua, an island in the Pacific. Local legend said that it had existed for thousands of years. 'But now,' he wrote, 'I've been told it is gone.'* Ask students: Where has Tebua gone? (It has disappeared as a result of rising sea levels). Why has it disappeared? (Rising sea levels are a result of global warming.) What other risks do places like Kiribati face? (Increasing numbers of tropical storms, threat of tsunami etc.)
2. Who can locate Kiribati on a blank map of the world? (Atlases might be needed here!) Who are Kiribati's nearest neighbours? What would life be like there? What threats do places like Kiribati face?

Ideas for plenaries

1. With books closed ask students to explain these terms to the class: environmental refugees, multiple hazards, greenhouse gases. Ask them to begin a dictionary of key terms for 'The world at risk' starting with this key vocabulary.
2. Use the 'What do you think?' on page 7 of the Student Book as a plenary to get students thinking about who emits the most greenhouse gases and who will suffer most from global warming.
3. Question time. Think back over the lesson and write down three questions related to what you have learned. The teacher will ask a member of the class to try to answer.

 Hazards and disasters

The unit in brief

This unit looks at what hazards and disasters are. For a natural event to become a hazard it has to involve people. A disaster is simply bigger than a natural hazard. Whether a hazard becomes a disaster can depend on how vulnerable the people are who are exposed to it.

A Background box explains that the hazards in this chapter are of two types: hydro-meteorological and geophysical.

Key ideas

- A natural hazard is a natural event or process which affects people, e.g. causing loss of life or injury, economic damage, disruption to people's lives, or environmental degradation.
- Hazards can be either hydro-meteorological or geophysical.
- A disaster is simply bigger than a natural hazard.
- Whether a hazard becomes a disaster can depend on how vulnerable the people who are exposed to it are.
- The greater the scale of the natural hazard, and the more exposed people are, the greater a disaster it is likely to be.

Unit outcomes

By the end of this unit most students should be able to:
- define natural hazard;
- classify events as hydrological, meteorological, geomorphological, or tectonic;
- understand the difference between a natural hazard and a disaster;
- give examples of vulnerable people;
- explain which type of natural disaster is most frequent.

Ideas for a starter

1. Ask students: What is a natural hazard? Who can give me a definition? Who can give me some examples of natural hazards?
2. Show students photos of natural events, e.g. avalanches like the photo on page 8 of the Student Book, and photos of natural hazards – with people clearly visible and affected by the event. What is the difference between a natural event and a hazard?

Ideas for plenaries

1. Make a graffiti wall of what students have learned today.
2. Use the 'What do you think?' on page 8 of the Student Book as a plenary.
3. Ask students to add the Key vocabulary for this unit to their dictionary of key terms for 'The world at risk'.
4. Write 'hazards and disasters' in the middle of the page. Create a mind map around the phrase. How many ideas can you come up with in 120 seconds?

 22   1: The world at risk   1: The world at risk   23

About the students' book

Matching the Edexcel specification

AS Geography for Edexcel has been written to meet the requirements of the specification. The chapter and unit headings in the students' book correspond to the topics in the specification, and we have pursued many of the suggestions in the 'Teaching and Learning' sections in the specification.

References to the specification

The Enquiry questions and 'What you need to learn' from the specification are detailed on the opening page for each chapter.

The chapter called 'Exams: how to be successful' at the end of the students' book tells students about the specification and the exams. It tells them how questions are marked, how marks are gained and lost, and offers guidance on question-answering technique.

Promoting best practice

Geography is very much about using a variety of resources to identify, describe, and explain the often multi-causal nature of geographical phenomena, and the students' book deliberately offers information and data in a number of ways. We hope the questions in the students' book will encourage students to approach diagrams, graphs, data tables, and photographs, and ideas and scenarios, in a questioning manner.

At the right level

We have tried to ensure that the definitions, descriptions, and explanations are clear and concise and appropriately pitched for the wide range of students now embarking on AS courses.

The material is intended to be accessible to all students, but we have also aimed to provide plenty of opportunity to stretch and challenge stronger students.

The questions cater for the full ability range, and provide plenty of scope for independent learning.

Interesting and relevant

Information is presented in a lively, thought-provoking way. The case studies are as current as possible at the time of writing, and are supported by good quality photographs. We hope we've achieved the right balance between breadth and depth.

There are questions for each unit in the students' book.

- 'Over to you' questions mostly provide students with opportunities for collaboration, for pair or group work.
- 'On your own' questions mostly provide students with opportunities for independent work.
- Resources and questions are quite closely linked, to encourage student learning to be active and enquiring. The questions cater for the full ability range.
- The students' book also contains 'exam-style' questions, with marks allocated. These are clearly identified. They are included in certain 'On your own' questions, and on the final page for each chapter. They give the chance of valuable exam practice.
- There are also 'What do you think?' boxes. These ask questions about controversial issues, and will challenge students' critical thinking. You could use them in a variety of ways – to spark classroom debate and discussion, or for homework. They are often recommended in the 'Ideas for plenaries' given in this book. Questions of this type will not appear in exam papers.
- The wide range of activities should encourage students to approach diagrams, graphs, data tables, and photographs, and ideas and scenarios, in a questioning manner.

Answers

The Activities and Planning OxBox CD-ROM provides answers for the 'Over to you' and 'On your own' questions.

It also provides model answers and mark schemes for the exam-style questions.

- flood___s are planned for ___rbank to protect built-up areas.
- there are plans to set aside 'reserves' of land, where flooding will be permitted and in which floodwater would be held naturally like a sponge.

Decisions are also needed now about longer-term flood protection and how the estuary can best be protected – whether the planned Thames Gateway developments go ahead or not.

Should housing be built in areas where there is a severe flood risk?

What do you think?

Over to you

1 In pairs, produce a spider diagram of the impacts of a major London flood on **a** London, **b** the UK as a whole.

2 Select either Holderness or the Dorset/Hampshire coast, or an area of coast known to you. Using atlases and OS maps, assess the potential risk from coastal flooding on **a** settlements, **b** industries, **c** the environment.

3 In pairs, draw up a list of social and environmental benefits of developing the Thames Gateway. Then list any potential problems or costs. Which is greater – costs or benefits?

On your own

4 Define the following: eustatic and isostatic change.

5 Research development plans (e.g. housing, jobs) for the Thames Gateway, using, for example, the London Development Agency website (www.lda.gov.uk). Include:
a planned flood defences
b whether these defences will be sufficient.
Use this to prepare a presentation either in favour of or against the developments.

Exam question: Explain how coastal flooding presents environmental, social and economic risks for the UK. (10 marks)

Matching the specification

Unit 1 Global challenges

Chapter 1 The world at risk

This topic has seven enquiry questions about risk; these are sub-grouped into two sections. Section A studies the risk from hazards. Section B explores risk in the context of climate change.

A The risk from hazards

Students need to know why some hazards are increasing, and different trends in hazards, e.g. lives lost versus damage caused.

They need to understand vulnerability and how this concept applies to hazards in different parts of the world.

They need to know how to research hazard risk in their local area.

They need to know that different hazards have different global distributions.

They need case study knowledge of California's coast and the Philippines.

Some examples used (e.g. Kiribati) can be used in assessing risks from climate change.

Examples used in the Student Book to study each key question are as follows:

1   **Global hazards: What are the main types of physical risks facing the world and how big a threat are they?**

- Kiribati, and hazards posed by global warming
- Classifying different hazards
- The hazard risk equation
- Vulnerable populations (Bam, Armenian, and Californian earthquakes, and the 2004 tsunami)

2   **Global hazard trends: How and why are natural hazards now becoming seen as an increasing global threat?**

- Numbers, trends, and the contrasts in people affected and economic damage caused by hazards
- The impact of the 2004 tsunami
- Australian bushfires – increased risk, but reducing lives lost

3   **Global hazard patterns: Why are some places more hazardous and disaster-prone than others?**

- The north London tornado; how to research and assess hazard risk in the local area
- Know the distribution of major hazards
- Assess the causes and impacts of hazards; California's coast and the Philippines

B Risk and climate change

The introduction to this section of the book is about process, rather than case study examples.

However, students do need case study knowledge about why some places may suffer more from the impacts of global warming than others; the Arctic and Africa are compulsory.

Students also need detailed knowledge of:
- how climate change is being addressed in different parts of the world
- countries that face a difficult future with global warming
- how carbon emissions can be reduced.

Examples used in the Student Book to study each key question are as follows:

4 Climate change and its causes: Is global warming a recent short-term phenomenon, or should it be seen as part of longer-term climate change?

- Examples of long-, medium-, and short-term climate change, and the evidence, e.g. past weather data, glacial and sea level change
- The enhanced greenhouse effect and greenhouse gases

5 The impacts of global warming: What are the impacts of climate change and why should we be concerned?

- Assessing the potential impacts of climate changes on the Arctic and Africa, Kiribati, Bangladesh, Indonesia
- Changes to the thermohaline circulation
- Evaluating different IPCC scenarios for the future
- Understanding 'tipping point' and its significance

6 Coping with climate change: What are the strategies for dealing with climate change?

- Evaluating approaches in mitigating and adapting to climate change
- How people can reduce carbon footprints
- Why Kyoto proved difficult to implement
- Strategies for dealing with climate change

7 The challenge of global hazards for the future: How should we tackle the global challenges of increasing risk and vulnerability in a more hazardous world?

- Why some countries will find it difficult to cope – e.g. Bangladesh, Indonesia
- The Stern Review and its recommendations
- Evaluating energy efficiency, e.g. nuclear energy, CHP, BedZED

Unit 1 Global challenges continued

This topic has seven enquiry questions, grouped into three sections, A, B, and C below.

A What globalisation means

This section uses examples (e.g. Disney) to show how globalisation occurs, how it has arisen, and its impacts.

Students do not need in-depth case studies for questions 1 and 2, though the use of examples such as Disney helps to understand complexity.

Detailed case study information will help for question 3.

Examples used in the Student Book to study each key question are as follows:

1 Globalisation: What is globalisation and how is it changing people's lives?

- Disney, the process of globalisation and its impacts
- Colonialism and the beginnings of globalisation

2 Global groupings: What are the main groupings of nations? What differences in levels of power and wealth exist?

- The emergence of a 'Third World'
- Using development indicators, e.g. economic (GNP) and social (HDI)
- Trading blocs and world trade

3 Global networks: Why, as places and societies become more interconnected, do some places show extreme wealth and poverty?

- The debt crisis and its impacts (Africa – Zambia, Tanzania, and Kenya)
- New winners and losers (China, India)
- Impacts of TNCs (supermarkets)

B How globalisation affects population in the UK and Europe

This section refers specifically to the UK and Europe, and students must study these areas.

It refers to the population dynamics of the UK, including its ageing population, patterns of migration from the Commonwealth, and recent arrivals from the eastern Europe.

Examples used in the Student Book to study each key question are as follows:

4 Roots: How does evidence from personal, local and national sources help us understand the pattern of population change in the UK?

- Increased life expectation, decreased fertility, and impacts on UK population structure
- The UK's ageing population
- Commonwealth migrants to the UK

5 On the move: How is migration changing the face of the EU?

- Commonwealth migration to the UK
- Migration within the EU – economic migrants and the 'new' EU
- Retirement flows to Spain

C The effects of globalisation on urban growth globally, and on people and the environment

6 World cities: What is driving the 'new' urbanisation? What are its consequences?

This question is focused on examples of two processes: suburbanisation and geographic expansion of western cities, and hyper-urbanisation of developing countries.

Specific case studies are required.

Students will need to study examples of a major city in each of the developed and developing world.

Examples used in the Student Book to study this are:
- The growth of Los Angeles and suburbanisation
- The rapid recent growth of Mumbai and shanty towns
- Sustainability issues for each

7 Global challenges for the future: What are the social and environmental consequences of globalisation? Can we manage these changes for a better world?

A general understanding is needed of the social and environmental impacts of globalisation; students need to study examples of these, and of different ways of reducing or improving each.

Examples used in the Student Book to study this are:
- Environmental impacts (deforestation, climate change, carbon footprints)
- Social impacts (cultural – Cuba)
- Reducing impacts (fair trade, ethical trade, carbon credits, recycling)

Unit 2 Geographical investigations

Unit 2 allows choice by teachers and/or students; one physical and one human option must be studied. You should ensure that fieldwork and research form a substantive part of teaching and learning. This is a research-focused part of the specification and students should be engaged in research for some of their learning. The exam will require that they have carried out their research and are able to understand its significance.

Chapter 3 Extreme weather

This topic focuses on weather events that appear to be 'one-offs', and how and why these occur, together with longer-term processes such as drought.

Examples with which students should be familiar include storms, drought, hurricanes, or wind storms.

They need to know the causes of such events and how well people manage and respond to them.

Examples used in the Student Book to study each key question are as follows:

1 Extreme weather watch: What are extreme weather conditions and how and why do they lead to extreme weather events?

- The 2003 heatwave, its causes, and impacts
- Longer-term trends in extreme weather events
- The causes of depressions, anticyclones

2 Extreme impacts: What are the impacts of extreme weather on people, the economy and the environment?

See enquiry question 3

3 Increasing risks: How are people and places increasingly at risk from and vulnerable to extreme weather?

The following studies take a common approach to meet the demands of enquiry questions 2 and 3; they require knowledge of impacts and of vulnerability.
- Bangladesh and countries with vulnerable populations
- The impacts of Hurricane Katrina, 2005; Boscastle 2004; the Severn floods, 2007; the Australian drought 2001-2007

4 Managing extreme weather: How can we best respond to and cope with the impacts of extreme weather?

This enquiry question requires knowledge of and an ability to evaluate how well people respond to threats of extreme weather.
- Boscastle and the Severn floods – responses and management
- Sustainable strategies for future management in St Ives, New Orleans, and water resources in the Murray-Darling basin

Unit 2 Geographical investigations continued

Chapter 4 Crowded coasts

This topic is about the ways in which coasts attract people, and the consequences of that growth.

It focuses mainly on two UK stretches of coast.

Students need detailed knowledge of two or three areas.

This chapter uses the Dorset and Hampshire coast (coastal pressures), Holderness (coastal erosion and its management) and the Thames Gateway (managing future growth).

Examples used in the Student Book to study each key question are as follows:

1 Competition for coasts: Why is the coastal zone so favoured for development?

- Growth and development of Bournemouth, Florida, Spain, and Australia's coast
- Researching sources to explain growth along named coastlines

2 Coping with pressure: How do various coastal developments create competition and conflict? How can these pressures be resolved?

- Pressures on the Dorset and Hampshire coast – pollution (Fawley) and tourism (Dorset World Heritage coast); threats to sand dunes (Studland), salt marshes (the Solent), and Dibden Bay

3 Increasing risks: How is coastal development increasingly at risk from and vulnerable to physical processes?

- The threat of rapid erosion (Holderness) and flooding (Thames estuary)
- Using primary and secondary sources to investigate the causes and impacts of coastal erosion

4 Coastal management: How is coastal management adapting to new ideas and situations?

- Coastal defences along the Holderness coast; how effective?
- Assessing sustainable approaches, e.g. Abbott's Farm

Unit 2 Geographical investigations continued

Chapter 5 Unequal spaces

This topic is about inequalities.

It looks at how inequalities exist within countries, and within cities and rural areas.

It draws upon a range of areas, though focuses primarily on rural inequalities in East Anglia and Botswana, and on urban inequalities in London and Botswana.

Throughout, students should research primary and secondary sources, e.g. census data, environmental quality, employment data, to identify and explain inequalities.

Examples used in the Student Book to study each key question are as follows:

1 Recognising inequality: What are unequal spaces and what causes them?

- Rural-urban inequalities in the UK
- Why inequality exists in East Anglia
- Inequalities within Botswana and the causes of these, e.g. HIV/AIDS

2 Inequality for whom? What impact do unequal spaces have on people?

- East Anglia, e.g. lack of employment, affordable housing, and services
- Botswana's rural areas – the marginalised Batswana and land rights
- Botswana's urban areas, e.g. Gaberone
- London's deprived inner cities, peripheral estates. Comparing Hackney and Hampstead

3 Managing rural inequalities: How can we manage rural inequality and improve the lives of the rural poor? How successful have particular schemes been?

- East Anglia, e.g. community transport, rural housing, jobs; focus on Blakenham and SnOasis
- Botswana – NDPs, and urban initiatives, e.g. housing self-help, sustainable tourism
- Evaluating rural schemes, e.g. self-help groups, services (e.g. dial-a-bus), mobile services, bottom-up strategies

4 Managing urban inequalities: What strategies can be used to combat inequality in urban areas? How successful have particular schemes been?

- Urban initiatives in London – e.g. Nightingale Estate
- The role of named key players, e.g. local authorities, groups and individuals
- Evaluating rural schemes, e.g. housing improvement, sustainable communities, reducing crime, transport

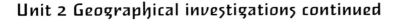

Unit 2 Geographical investigations continued

Chapter 6 Rebranding places

This topic is about the way in which places are re-developed and marketed so that they gain a new identity.

Fundamental to this is economic change and responding to the 'new economy'.

The two threads are **a** urban and **b** rural rebranding.

Detailed case study knowledge is needed for both areas.

Throughout, students should research primary and secondary sources, e.g. census data, environmental quality, employment data, to identify and evaluate rebranding strategies.

Examples used in the Student Book to study each key question are as follows:

1 Time to rebrand: What is rebranding and why is it needed in some places?

- Rebranding towns and cities (East London, Sydney, Manchester, Walton-on-the-Naze) and rural areas (e.g. farming, tourism, culture)

2 Rebranding strategies: Who are the 're-branding players' and what strategies exist for places to improve themselves?

- The players involved, e.g. private firms, sponsors, government agencies, the EU
- How these players affect urban flagship schemes, e.g. London Olympics, London's Docklands, Stratford City, Manchester
- Evaluating these for sustainability

3 Managing rural rebranding: How successful has rebranding been in the countryside?

- Cornwall and Objective One investment in rural enterprise, e.g. the Eden Project, development of tourism (Extreme Academy), farm diversification (Lobb's Farm Shop)

4 Managing urban rebranding: How successful have urban areas been in rebranding themselves?

- Knowing how to research rural and urban rebranding areas, e.g. surveys, questionnaires
- Evaluating the success of schemes on grounds of, for example, cost-benefit and sustainability

Integrating fieldwork and research into the course

Fieldwork and research skills are a key feature of Unit 2 Geographical investigations. Students will be expected to have carried out research both in the field and in class. The case for fieldwork is two-fold:

- its curriculum value as a means of helping students to learn;
- its assessment value whereby students will be asked to use fieldwork strategies in answering exam questions – those who have not had fieldwork experience will be at a definite disadvantage.

What kind of fieldwork?

Depending upon which units are chosen for study in Unit 2, fieldwork opportunities will vary. The requirements are clear in the specification, so that there are clear opportunities for students to engage in studies of:

- Extreme weather events – their impacts, and how people respond.
- Coastal environments – human pressures and management issues along 'crowded coasts', issues arising from coastal erosion or coastal flooding.
- Unequal spaces – evidence of inequalities (e.g. social, economic, or environmental) in rural or urban environments, together with evaluation of attempts to resolve these.
- Rebranding places – attempts to rebrand rural and urban environments, together with an evaluation of these.

In each case, work can be enhanced by the collection of primary data in the field, supported with secondary data collected in class or private study. However, the exam will be less about 'what?' students have studied, and more about 'how?' Students should therefore be given opportunities to:

- **Plan** a short investigation, or part of an investigation, so that they begin to understand the questions for enquiry, and the link between these questions and how data are collected.
- **Devise methods** of collecting data – e.g. interviews, questionnaires – or of evaluating those devised by their teachers.
- **Record data** by various means, manually or electronically, using a variety of strategies, e.g. Environmental Quality Surveys.
- **Present data**, and know why some methods are more appropriate than others for particular types of data.
- **Interpret and analyse data**, not simply by text but by using techniques such as rankings (including weighted ranking), cost-benefit, and so on.
- **Draw conclusions** from the data.
- **Evaluate** their findings in terms of validity, and their methods used.
- **Consider success criteria** for evaluating their fieldwork and plan further possible questions for study.

Making time for fieldwork and research

Time is pressured during the AS year, and some senior management teams in school may resist allowing fieldwork in school time if it no longer contributes to coursework. Consider therefore the kind of fieldwork you want to do:

- **Residential fieldwork** is suitable for lengthy investigations or where you want to teach a number of topics in a short, intensive time away. This is ideal for intensive coverage of parts of the course.
- **Days out** spread through the year can be very useful in that you are likely to get more of them, and therefore you can thread fieldwork techniques and approaches through the course. They also assist in providing variety – e.g. coastal and urban environments.

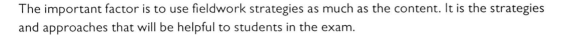

The important factor is to use fieldwork strategies as much as the content. It is the strategies and approaches that will be helpful to students in the exam.

Preparing students for fieldwork and research questions in the exam

Whichever topics students have studied, they will be expected to use fieldwork and research in the exam. Note particularly that fieldwork questions are very likely to be about methods or processes of collecting and analysing data and research, and not content. Exam questions will look something like this:

Example for 'Crowded coasts'

*Describe and explain **a programme of fieldwork and research** you would use to investigate the impacts of either coastal erosion or coastal flooding, along a stretch of coastline. (15 marks)*

Try preparing students by following three steps:

Step 1   Read and understand the question
This is a complex question and it would be easy for students to write a lot and gain few marks. To avoid this, two skills are essential:
- Read the question. It is not 'all they know about a stretch of coast', but about how they would **investigate the impacts** of coastal flooding or coastal erosion.
- Guide students towards underlining command words so that they do what the question asks.

Step 2   Focus the question
Students should focus on either coastal erosion or coastal flooding along a stretch of coast.
- They **must** mention a named stretch of coast – examiners only award about half marks for generalised answers that do not refer to places.
- If they choose flooding, it must be a coastal flood – an inland flood will not do.

Step 3   Answer the question
To answer the question, students do not need to have visited the coast – simply researched it. Fieldwork gets credit, but so too does secondary research. They might never have visited Holderness, but instead seen videos, used textbook material, and carried out their own research.
- Research could include photos of impacts of erosion, news articles about coastal flooding, or a survey about which methods of flood protection proved most effective in a recent coastal flood.
- It is the **programme** of research that students should describe – what they would do first, then second, and so on. At each stage they should give reasons.
- Focus the programme on **impacts** – which can be classified as economic, social and environmental:
  - **Economic** impacts might include damage caused, or transport disruption, using news websites (with examples).
  - **Social** impacts are about people – perhaps using a questionnaire in the field. Think of questions that could be asked, and why.
  - **Environmental** impacts might include visual impacts of coastal erosion, using, for example,

Credit will be given for
- naming a stretch of coast studied;
- describing an outline programme in stages, and explaining a rationale for this;
- focusing each stage on **what** they would do and then **why**. For example: 'I would select a local newspaper such as the Western Morning News to find out how local emergency services coped with the flood in Torquay because this would show how they rescued people, together with photos of the flood.'

Use these same approaches for questions in other topics – examples include:

Example for 'Extreme weather'	*Describe and explain a programme of fieldwork and research you would use to investigate the links between precipitation and flooding along a stretch of river. (15 marks)*
Example for 'Unequal spaces'	*Describe the results of your fieldwork and research into how to reduce inequality, and explain how these help you to judge the success of either the urban or rural schemes involved. (15 marks)*
Example for 'Rebranding places'	*Describe the results of your fieldwork and research into urban rebranding, and explain how these help you to judge the success of the schemes involved. (15 marks)*

1 The world at risk

About the topic

This topic has two strands:

1 The risks from hazards
   - There are two main types of hazards – hydrometeorlogical and geophysical.
   - Hazards can become natural disasters where the population is vulnerable.
   - Hazard hotspots show that the poor lose lives while the rich lose money.
2 Risk and climate change
   - The causes of global warming, relationship to long-term climate change, and impacts.
   - Possible solutions.

About the chapter

- This chapter investigates hazards and disasters, how they increasingly threaten people's lives and property, and the idea of vulnerability.
- It looks at hazard hotspots, with the Philippines and California used as case studies. It investigates causes and effects of climate change and looks at the impacts of global warming on the Arctic and Africa.
- Dealing with climate change, mitigation and adaptation, options for the future, and strategies for dealing with climate change are included.
- The chapter ends with case studies of Bangladesh and Indonesia which explore how these two countries tackle risk and vulnerability.

Key vocabulary

There is no set list of words in the specification that students must know. However, examiners will use some or all of the following words in the examinations, and would expect students to know them and use them in their answers.

adaptation	Milankovitch cycles
boreal forest	mitigation
carbon credits	multiple hazards
carbon offsetting	natural hazard
carbon sequestration	North Atlantic Drift
carbon sinks	permafrost
deep sea core samples	positive ice-albedo feedback
destructive boundary	pyroclastic flows
disaster	radiation
enhanced greenhouse effect	saline
environmental refugees	scenario
exponential	subducted
geomorphological	tectonic
global conveyor belt	thermohaline circulation
greenhouse effect	tipping point
greenhouse gases	tree line
hazard vulnerability	tundra
IPCC	vent
lahars	volcanic emissions
magma chamber	vulnerable populations
mega-delta	

The glossary at the end of this book contains many of these words and phrases. For students, the key word boxes in the chapter or the glossary at the end of the Student Book will help them with the meanings of all.

1.1 What has happened to Tebua?

The unit in brief

This 2-page unit acts as an introduction to the topic 'The world at risk' and investigates the risks facing some of the world's most remote island nations. Tebua (one of the islands of Kiribati) in the Pacific Ocean has disappeared – swallowed by rising sea levels. The rest of Kiribati is also suffering from rising sea levels and erosion. People are leaving, becoming the world's first environmental refugees. Rising sea levels are a result of global warming, and along with increases in the number of tropical storms the region suffers from the threat of multiple hazards.

Key ideas

- Rising sea levels are threatening low-lying island nations such as Kiribati in the Pacific.
- People forced to migrate as a result of changes to the environment are called environmental refugees.
- Tebua's disappearance is one sign that global warming is happening.
- Kiribati is in a region at risk from multiple hazards.
- The worst effects of global warming are felt by the poorest countries who make the least contribution to the problem and are least equipped to deal with it.

Unit outcomes

By the end of this unit most students should be able to:
- explain why rising sea levels are threatening nations such as Kiribati;
- define the term environmental refugees;
- suggest why large numbers of environmental refugees could create a political problem in countries such as Australia and New Zealand;
- say how far Kiribati is a nation facing multiple hazards.

Ideas for a starter

1 Show students the photo of Tarawa Atoll on page 6 of the Student Book. Read the first part of the text out loud, i.e. *Early in 2002, writer Curtis A. Moore went in search of Tebua, an island in the Pacific. Local legend said that it had existed for thousands of years. 'But now,' he wrote, 'I've been told it is gone.'* Ask students: Where has Tebua gone? (It has disappeared as a result of rising sea levels). Why has it disappeared? (Rising sea levels are a result of global warming.) What other risks do such places face? (Increasing numbers of tropical storms, threat of tsunami etc.)

2 Who can locate Kiribati on a blank map of the world? (Atlases might be needed here!) Who are Kiribati's nearest neighbours? What would life be like there? What threats do places like Kiribati face?

Ideas for plenaries

1 With books closed ask students to explain these terms to the class: environmental refugees, multiple hazards, greenhouse gases. Ask them to begin a dictionary of key terms for 'The world at risk' starting with this key vocabulary.

2 Use the 'What do you think?' on page 7 of the Student Book as a plenary to get students thinking about who emits the most greenhouse gases and who will suffer most from global warming

3 Question time. Think back over the lesson and write down three questions related to what you have learned. The teacher will ask a member of the class to try to answer.

The unit in brief

This unit looks at what hazards and disasters are. For a natural event to become a hazard it has to involve people. A disaster is simply bigger than a natural hazard. Whether a hazard becomes a disaster can depend on how vulnerable the people are who are exposed to it.

A Background box explains that the hazards in this chapter are of two types: hydro-meteorological and geophysical.

Key ideas

- A natural hazard is a natural event or process which affects people, e.g. causing loss of life or injury, economic damage, disruption to people's lives, or environmental degradation.
- Hazards can be either hydro-meteorological or geophysical.
- A disaster is simply bigger than a natural hazard.
- Whether a hazard becomes a disaster can depend on how vulnerable the people who are exposed to it are.
- The greater the scale of the natural hazard, and the more exposed people are, the greater a disaster it is likely to be.

Unit outcomes

By the end of this unit most students should be able to:
- define natural hazard;
- classify events as hydrological, meteorological, geomorphological, or tectonic;
- understand the difference between a natural hazard and a disaster;
- give examples of vulnerable people;
- explain which type of natural disaster is most frequent.

Ideas for a starter

1 Ask students: What is a natural hazard? Who can give me a definition? Who can give me some examples of natural hazards?
2 Show students photos of natural events, e.g. avalanches like the photo on page 8 of the Student Book, and photos of natural hazards – with people clearly visible and affected by the event. What is the difference between a natural event and a hazard?

Ideas for plenaries

1 Make a graffiti wall of what students have learned today.
2 Use the 'What do you think?' on page 8 of the Student Book as a plenary.
3 Ask students to add the Key vocabulary for this unit to their dictionary of key terms for 'The world at risk'.
4 Write 'hazards and disasters' in the middle of the page. Create a mind map around the phrase. How many ideas can you come up with in 120 seconds?

The unit in brief

The first spread of this 4-page unit looks at whether the world is becoming a more hazardous place, and who suffers most from natural disasters. The second spread investigates the world's worst hazards, which hazards are most common, which have the worst impacts, and why floods and windstorms are increasing. The unit is backed up with a large number of graphs, tables and maps showing trends in numbers of natural disasters, economic and social costs, global distributions of natural disasters and people affected as well as the worst natural disasters, numbers of most common disasters, and so on.

Key ideas

- The number of reported natural disasters rose sharply between 1930 and 2006.
- Early hazard prediction can reduce the number of deaths from disasters, but economic losses have rocketed.
- The number of people affected by natural disasters has risen sharply. Floods and windstorms account for 75% of natural disasters.
- Most deaths from natural disasters occur in Asia.
- In terms of impacts: earthquakes cause occasional major damage but are not increasing; damaging floods are increasing, but not in a consistent way; damaging windstorms are increasing, but not consistently.
- The increase in floods and windstorms could be due to global warming or in the case of windstorms could be part of a natural cycle.

Unit outcomes

By the end of this unit most students should be able to:
- use graphs to outline the trends in numbers of natural disasters, deaths, and economic damage;
- suggest why the numbers of disasters has increased but deaths have fallen;
- be aware that single events can have a dramatic impact on the economic cost and number of deaths from disasters;
- explain why the number of people affected by natural disasters has risen sharply;
- suggest why Asia has the greatest number of deaths from natural disasters;
- give two possible reasons for the increase in floods and windstorms.

Ideas for a starter

1. Show students a video clip of a recent natural disaster. Ask questions to set the scene for the unit. Who suffers most from natural disasters? Which hazards are most common? Are natural disasters increasing?
2. Give students facts and figures about a recent natural disaster in terms of its location; deaths and people affected; value of damage caused.
3. There is a wealth of data provided in this unit. Any of the graphs, maps or tables could be used to kick off the unit.

Ideas for plenaries

1. 'Over to you' Activities **4** and **5** could b used as a plenary.
2. Use 'What do you think?' on page 12 of the Student Book to round up the unit.
3. Did you find anything difficult about the work in this unit? What? Why? What could help to make it less difficult?

The unit in brief

This 6-page unit looks at the idea of vulnerability and why hazards affect people and places in different ways. It begins by looking at how significant natural hazards are in terms of the number of deaths recorded from natural disasters. It then compares four earthquakes to illustrate that the effects of disasters are felt the most by those people who are most vulnerable. The unit includes a case study of the Boxing Day tsunami to further investigate the idea of vulnerability.

Key ideas

- Some places are more vulnerable than others to natural disasters.
- When disasters occur it is vulnerable people who suffer the most.
- Vulnerability is based on three factors.
- The Boxing Day tsunami was at the scale of disaster that occurs about once in every 100 years.
- The countries which suffered most in the Boxing Day tsunami were those where tourism had grown rapidly in recent years, meaning coastal mangrove swamps had been cleared.

Unit outcomes

By the end of this unit most students should be able to:
- understand that some places are more vulnerable to natural disasters than others;
- understand the disaster risk formula;
- explain why certain groups of people were much more vulnerable to the effects of the tsunami in Sri Lanka than the population as a whole;
- describe the factors that vulnerability is based on;
- explain the importance of maintaining coastal mangrove swamps.

Ideas for a starter

1 Recap: What do we mean by vulnerable populations? Why are people vulnerable to hazards?
2 Show students the photo of the tsunami wall of water hitting Ao Nang in Thailand on page 17 of the Student Book. What can they say about it? Lead discussion on to the impacts on people and the idea of vulnerability.

Ideas for plenaries

1 Use 'On your own' activity **8** on page 19 as a debate. Students can then use the ideas generated to write an essay afterwards.
2 Use the 'What do you think?' on page 19 as a plenary.
3 Ask students what was the single biggest insight they had from this unit.

The unit in brief

This 2-page unit explores bushfires in Australia. It includes a Background box explaining how bushfires start and how they spread, and looks at how deaths from bushfires have been reduced by controlled burning and education programmes.

Key ideas

- Bushfires mostly start as a result of carelessness and lightning strikes.
- Bushfires can spread as ground fires, crown fires, and spot fires.
- Bushfires cause significant damage to property, but the number of deaths has fallen steadily.
- Two methods used to cut deaths and increase safety are controlled burning and education programmes.

Unit outcomes

By the end of this unit most students should be able to:
- understand how bushfires start and spread;
- describe the methods used to cuts deaths and increase safety from bushfires;
- identify the problems and benefits of controlled burning.

Ideas for a starter

1 Ask students to close their eyes and play a mind movie in their heads. A bushfire is approaching. What can they see? What can they hear and smell? What is going to happen?
2 Show images of Australian bushfires. Ask students: Why do they happen? What damage do they cause? What can we do about them? Do other countries suffer similar fires?

Ideas for plenaries

1 'On your own' activity **5** could be us as a plenary.
2 Prepare an odd-one-out for your partner on what you have learned today.
3 Use the 'What do you think?' on page 20 of the Student Book as a plenary.

The unit in brief

In this 2-page unit students will asses hazard risks in their own area using London as an example. We usually associate tornadoes with the American Midwest, and yet the UK has over 70 tornado events every year. A localised tornado hit Kensal Rise in London in December 2006. A Background box explains what causes the UK's storms and local tornadoes. However, London's biggest hazard is flooding. The Thames Flood Barrier was completed in 1982. Its purpose is to prevent incoming tides from flooding the city when storm water may be flowing away. But it is now too small and needs replacing as sea levels continue to rise due to global warming.

Key ideas

- The UK has over 70 tornado events every year.
- Although there are differences, tornadoes are like mini depressions with temperature and pressure differences in a small area.
- The biggest hazard London faces is flooding.
- There are four main causes for flooding in London.
- The Thames Flood Barrier needs replacing due to sea level rise.

Unit outcomes

By the end of this unit most students should be able to:
- explain how tornadoes and depressions form;
- describe the four causes of flooding in London;
- understand why the Thames Flood Barrier needs replacing;
- assess the impacts of hazards in the local area.

Ideas for a starter

1 Show students a video clip of a tornado in action. Ask: Does this happen in the UK? The answer is yes, and more often than students might think.
2 Search Google to find images of London under water, e.g. the London Eye, the Houses of Parliament, St Paul's Cathedral etc. Ask: Could this happen? How can it be prevented? Does London need more protection? Why?

Ideas for plenaries

1 Starter **2** could be used as a plenary if not already used.
2 Use the 'What do you think?' on page 23 of the Student Book. Why is London so important that it should possibly have its own hazards budget?
3 Students can work together to write a paragraph on London's flood risk.

1.7 Hazard hotspots

The unit in brief

This is a 6-page unit in which students find out about multiple hazards in two hazard hotspots. The Philippines is exposed to tectonic hazards, tsunami, typhoons, and landslides. A Background box explains the tectonic hazards. Two examples of hazard events are included: the Mount Pinatubo eruption in 1991 and the Guinsaugon landslide in 2006. California is the USA's most hazardous state, the reasons being plate tectonics and climate patterns related to El Niño and La Niña. A Background box explains El Niño and La Niña. Two examples of earthquakes are included Loma Prieta in San Francisco in 1989, and the 1994 Northridge earthquake in Los Angeles.

Key ideas

- The Philippines is exposed to tectonic hazards, tsunami, typhoons, and landslides.
- The Philippines lies on a destructive plate boundary.
- Some hazard risks in the Philippines have multiple effects.
- California is at risk from earthquakes and climate patterns related to El Niño and La Niña.
- San Francisco lies along the San Andreas fault, a conservative plate boundary.
- Wealthy countries suffer mostly from economic damage from hazards, in poorer countries the impacts are greatest on people.

Unit outcomes

By the end of this unit most students should be able to:
- explain why the Philippines and California face multiple hazards;
- classify and compare the impacts of the Mount Pinatubo eruption and the Loma Prieta and Northridge earthquakes;
- Recognise that wealthy countries suffer mostly from economic damage from hazards while in poorer countries people suffer more;
- explain the impact of La Niña and El Niño on California.

Ideas for a starter

1 On a blank map of the world mark on the Philippines and California. What do they have in common? They are both hazard hotspots. Explore with students what they think this means.
2 Brainstorm different hazards. Which hazards have the greatest impact in terms of numbers of people killed, made homeless and damage in economic terms? Compare students responses with the table on page 26 of the Student Book which summarises the impacts of various hazards on the Philippines between 2000 and 2006.
3 Show students the photo of the San Andreas fault on page 27 of the Student Book. What is this? How does it move? What impact will its movement have?

Ideas for plenaries

1 With books closed ask students to define the key vocabulary from this unit. Then ask them to add it to their dictionary of key terms for 'The world at risk'.
2 'Hazard hotspots are …' Go round the class asking students to add to the phrase without repetition or hesitation. If they repeat themselves or hesitate another student takes over. They have one minute on the topic.
3 Use either of the 'What do you think?' suggestions on pages 27 and 28 of the Student Book as plenaries. The one on page 27 can be used with the table on page 26.

The unit in brief

This unit investigates the causes of climate change and global warming. The first two pages look at the natural greenhouse effect, greenhouse gases, and their contribution to global warming and the enhanced greenhouse effect. The next two pages consider whether global warming is part of a natural cycle of climate change and considers changes in solar output, variations in the earth's orbit, cosmic collision, and volcanic emissions. It also looks at the accuracy of weather recording and evidence that shows that climate is changing.

Key ideas

- There is no dispute about the fact that global warming is happening, but there is debate about how and why it is happening.
- The greenhouse effect is a completely natural process.
- Carbon dioxide, chlorofluorocarbons, methane, nitrous oxide, and ozone are all greenhouse gases which contribute to global warming.
- The enhanced greenhouse effect is the increase in the natural greenhouse effect, said to be caused by human activities which increase the quantity of greenhouse gases in the atmosphere.
- Climate has alternated between cold glacial periods and warmer periods since the Pleistocene period.

Unit outcomes

By the end of this unit most students should be able to:
- understand that not everyone agrees how and why global warming is happening;
- explain the greenhouse effect;
- give four examples of greenhouse gases and explain their contribution to global warming;
- draw a diagram to show the enhanced greenhouse effect;
- describe how changes in solar output, variations in the earth's orbit, cosmic collisions, and volcanic emissions may have affected climate.

Ideas for a starter

1 Show the diagram of the greenhouse effect on the whiteboard minus the labels. Ask students to add the labels: carbon dioxide and other gases, sun, solar radiation, reflected heat, radiated heat, re-radiated heat, increasing greenhouse gases absorb and re-radiate heat on the diagram.

2 Ask: Who can tell me what the greenhouse effect is? What is the enhanced greenhouse effect? What are greenhouse gases?

Ideas for plenaries

1 Use 'Over to you' activities 1 and 2 as a plenary.

2 The 'What do you think?' on page 32 of the Student Book can be used as a plenary and debate on the importance of the causes of global warming.

3 Write down as many words as you can relating to this unit. Then add the key vocabulary to your dictionary of key terms for this chapter.

The effects of climate change

The unit in brief

This 4-page unit begins by exploring at the effects of climate change on Greenland and goes on to look at changing global temperatures. Temperatures are rising globally but are not increasing at the same rate everywhere as the map on page 35 of the Student Book shows. The Arctic Ocean shows the greatest effects of climate change in terms of changing salinity and increasing river flows and this could affect global climate. Changes in the polar oceans are affecting their ability to act as carbon sinks.

Key ideas

- The area of Greenland's ice sheets melting each summer has increased by 30% since 1975.
- Global temperatures are increasing faster and exponentially.
- Temperatures are not increasing at the same rate everywhere.
- The ocean circulation called the thermohaline circulation (also known as the global conveyor belt) is being disturbed and could affect the North Atlantic Drift.
- Increases in the amount of fresh water flowing into the Arctic could affect the climate of the whole of Northern Europe.
- The Southern Ocean is one of the world's most important carbon sinks but changes mean that CO_2 is released into the atmosphere.

Unit outcomes

By the end of this unit most students should be able to:
- use the graph to describe the rate of temperature change from 1860;
- describe the variations in global temperature change;
- draw a sketch map to show why the Arctic is becoming less saline, why river flow is increasing, and how these might affect the North Atlantic Drift;
- construct a diagram to show the possible consequences if the North Atlantic Drift stopped;
- describe the changes in the polar oceans.

Ideas for a starter

1 Ask a student to read out the text entitled 'Warming island' to introduce the unit. Why is Greenland's ice cap melting faster?

2 Show students the graph on page 35 of the Student Book and/or the photos on page 34. What do they show? How far do they provide evidence of global warming?

Ideas for plenaries

1 Use 'On your own' activity **7** to open up a class debate on global warming. Students could then write a 500-word report summing up the debate.

2 Get students to add the key vocabulary from this unit to their dictionary of key terms for 'The world at risk'.

3 Provide students with 2 copies of the diagram of the thermohaline circulation on page 36 of the Student Book. Ask them to annotate one to show how the thermohaline circulation works. The other one should be annotated to show how changing salinity will affect the circulation and the North Atlantic Drift.

The impacts of global warming

The unit in brief

This 6-page unit looks at the impacts of global warming on the Arctic and Africa. The Arctic climate is unbelievably cold, but increasing temperatures are melting the Arctic ice. The unit looks at impacts on the environment, fish stocks and polar bears (both in danger) and the socio-economic impacts of global warming on the 155 000 Inuit who live in the Arctic. The 3 pages on Africa consider the evidence for global warming in Africa and consider why Africa is vulnerable. Students investigate the human and physical impacts of global warming in Africa and the link between global warming and debt.

Key ideas

- The rate of Arctic ice melt has risen substantially due to the positive ice-albedo feedback.
- Global warming in the Arctic has impacts on the environment, on fish stocks and polar bears and socio-economic impacts on the Inuit.
- There may be benefits to global warming in the Arctic – but even these can create additional problems.
- Africa is steadily warming, but not at the same rate everywhere.
- The main impacts of global warming on Africa will be human, but there are also physical impacts.
- The debt crisis is one of the main reasons why Africa is vulnerable to global warming.

Unit outcomes

By the end of this unit most students should be able to:

- classify the impacts of global warming on Inuit communities;
- describe some of the benefits of global warming in the Arctic, but understand that these may bring additional problems;
- describe the changes in temperature and predicted changes in rainfall in Africa;
- draw a diagram to show the links between global warming, changing rainfall patterns, impacts on food supply, and debt in Africa;
- explain how the increased likelihood of malaria will impact on the poverty trap.

Ideas for a starter

1. Show students 2 images – the area occupied by Arctic ice in the 1970s or 80s, and current ice coverage. Ask students what the likely impacts are of the decline in ice.
2. Show students a photo of a polar bear on an ice floe – the one in the Student Book on page 39, or something similar. Ask 'What has this got to do with global warming?'
3. For the section on Africa, read out the Oxfam quote on page 41. Ask: Why?
4. Show students the photo on page 41 of the Student Book. Is this Africa's future?

Ideas for plenaries

1. Give students a blank map of the Arctic area. Give them 5 minutes to annotate the map with the impacts of global warming.
2. Use the 'What do you think?' on page 39 of the Student Book as a plenary to get students to start thinking critically about whether global warming really matters.
3. Ask: What is the link between global warming and Africa's debt crisis?
4. Africa will suffer from global warming but its countries are not among those which emit the most greenhouse gases. Use the 'What do you think?' on page 42 to debate whether those countries that emit the most greenhouse gases should help Africa.

The unit in brief

This 2-page unit looks at the IPCC's belief that they have the evidence that shows that climate is changing as a result of human activity. The world has two main approaches to deal with climate change – mitigation and adaptation, and the unit considers the arguments for each.

Key ideas

- The IPCC believes that the evidence for climate change as a result of human activity is overwhelming.
- There are two main approaches for the world to deal with climate change – mitigation and adaptation.
- Mitigation of global warming refers to policies that are meant to delay, reduce, or prevent climate changes caused by global warming.
- Adaptation to global warming refers to policies which are designed to reduce the existing impacts of global warming.
- There are arguments for both mitigation and adaptation.

Unit outcomes

By the end of this unit most students should be able to:

- explain why the IPCC believes that the evidence for climate change as a result of human activity is overwhelming;
- explain the terms mitigation and adaptation;
- decide which are the strongest arguments for mitigation and adaptation and justify their choice.

Ideas for a starter

1 Ask students: What does mitigation mean? What does adaptation mean? Show them the photos on pages 44 and 45 of the Student Book to introduce the ideas of mitigation and adaptation in relation to global warming.
2 Who can tell me what the IPCC is? What do they do?

Ideas for plenaries

1 Get students to add the terms mitigation and adaptation to their dictionary of key terms to do with 'The world at risk'.
2 Use 'Over to you' activity 2 (the debate) as a plenary.
3 The 'What do you think?' on page 45 of the Student Book could be used as a plenary.
4 Make up 10-15 statements about climate change based on what students have learned so far, some true some false. Ask students to identify the false ones and correct them.

The unit in brief

The first 2 pages of this unit look at the scenarios predicted by the IPCC regarding greenhouse gas emissions. The second 2 pages consider whether the world has already reached 'tipping point' and look at the key features of the Stern Review.

Key ideas

- The IPCC collected evidence in the 1990s which showed that global warming was really happening.
- The IPCC has predicted 4 different scenarios regarding greenhouse gas emissions and climate change.
- The tipping point refers to a point beyond which the Earth cannot recover from the effects of carbon emissions, even with drastic action.
- A further tiny increase in global temperatures could have catastrophic consequences in terms of rising sea levels; shutting down the Atlantic thermohaline circulation; falling agricultural yields and water shortages.
- The 2006 Stern Review focused on the impacts of global warming and the actions needed to deal with them.

Unit outcomes

By the end of this unit most students should be able to:
- analyse the IPCC scenarios and decide what will make the best and worst scenarios happen;
- explain why the IPCC fears reaching a tipping point;
- describe the consequences of a further rise in global temperature;
- outline the key features of the Stern Review.

Ideas for a starter

1 Show students the graph on page 46 of the Student Book. Explain that it shows different scenarios predicted by the IPCC regarding greenhouse gas emissions. Ask: How does A1a suggest the world is producing energy? What kind of situation could produce B1?
2 Recap: What is the IPCC? What do they do?

Ideas for plenaries

1 Ask students to define the tipping point. What will cause the world to reach the tipping point? What impacts will it have?
2 Use the 'What do you think?' on page 48 of the Student Book as a way of introducing the next unit which looks at strategies for dealing with climate change.
3 Use the two photos on page 48 to discuss impacts of global warming.
4 What was the single biggest insight you gained from this unit?

The unit in brief

This 6-page unit investigates a variety of ways of reducing the impacts of climate change. It looks at how individuals can make a difference and uses the example of Coldplay offsetting emissions created during production, manufacture, and distribution of their albums by financing the planting of trees and forest development. It looks at the efforts of the European Emissions Trading Scheme to reduce greenhouse gas emissions and provides examples of carbon offsetting in action. It includes the Kyoto Protocol as an example of a global agreement to reduce greenhouse gas emissions.

Key ideas

- Individuals can take action to control climate change, but may not always be willing to pay for it.
- The Stern Review argued that people should pay for carbon in order to realise its importance.
- Reductions in greenhouse gas emissions can be achieved – but at a cost.
- The European Emissions Trading Scheme aims to reduce greenhouse gas emissions.
- Carbon offsetting is the name given to a credit system called carbon credits which aims to reduce greenhouse gas emissions.
- The Kyoto Protocol is a global agreement setting targets for reducing greenhouse gas emissions.

Unit outcomes

By the end of this unit most students should be able to:
- explain why people should pay for carbon emissions;
- understand that it may be more expensive to reduce emissions;
- describe the aims of the ETS and why it has failed;
- give two examples of carbon offsetting in action;
- assess the success of the Kyoto Protocol.

Ideas for a starter

1 Ask: What is the link between Coldplay and climate change? You could even play a track from 'A rush of blood to the head' or 'X&Y' to introduce this unit and ask the same question. You are looking for students to identify Coldplay's attempts to offset the carbon emissions from the production, manufacture, and distribution of their albums.

2 Ask: If you had the choice, who would rather travel by train or plane? Tell students that flying will do 10 times more environmental damage than travelling by train. Compare results from the class with the introductory text on page 50 of the Student Book, where when BA passengers were offered the chance to travel by train most preferred to fly.

Ideas for plenaries

1 'Over to you' activities **1** and **2** could be used as a plenary.

2 If you want to have a debate or discussion use 'What do you think?' on page 55 of the Student Book, or 'Over to you' activity **4**.

3 Take two minutes with a partner and think up one question about dealing with climate change that has not been covered in this unit. Others in the class can try to answer.

Energy use, efficiency and conservation

The unit in brief

This is a 4-page unit which considers strategies to combat climate change through energy efficiency and conservation. The UK wastes huge amounts of energy and the unit includes the example of Copenhagen's combined heat and power plant as a system for energy production which is clean, cheap, and efficient. Will new nuclear power stations be built in the UK to provide us with energy? The advantages and disadvantages are included here. Carbon sequestration and BedZED, an energy conservation project, are also included in this unit.

Key ideas

- Vast amounts of energy are wasted in the UK – even in the most efficient electricity power stations.
- Copenhagen's' combined heat and power system produces low CO_2 emissions, is cheap, and efficient.
- Nuclear energy is controversial but produces far lower greenhouse gas emissions than fossil fuels.
- Less than 3% of the UK's annual CO_2 emissions are being offset by the UK's woodlands.
- Households in the UK emit 27% of greenhouse gases and use 33% of energy consumed. BedZED is one example of an energy conservation project.

Unit outcomes

By the end of this unit most students should be able to:
- understand why greenhouse gas emissions should be reduced now;
- explain why huge amounts of energy are wasted in the UK;
- assess the advantages and disadvantages of using energy more efficiently; replacing the UK's existing nuclear power stations with new ones; conserving and reducing energy consumption with schemes such as BedZED; expanding the UK's forests.

Ideas for a starter

1 Find an image (e.g. infra red or a thermal image) of heat or energy loss from a house (try Google images). Use it to show students how we waste energy.
2 Ask students: What are the advantages and disadvantages of nuclear power? Record student responses in a table.

Ideas for plenaries

1 If you used starter **2** compare students' responses with the table on page 57 of the Student Book.
2 Use the 'What do you think?' on page 58 to generate a discussion on cutting emissions.
3 Ask for a definition of carbon sequestration.

The unit in brief

In this unit students find out about the risks facing Bangladesh. Bangladesh is the world's most densely populated country and lies on the flood plains of three major rivers. 60% of the country is 1 metre or less above sea level and Bangladesh not only faces risks from flooding but is now increasingly threatened by global warming. The unit looks at the options Bangladesh has to adapt to global warming.

Key ideas

- Bangladesh has a high, dense population; it lies on the flood plains of three major rivers and 60% of the country is 1 metre or less above sea level.
- Bangladesh is at risk from flooding as a result of Himalayan snowmelt, monsoon rains, and coastal flooding.
- Bangladesh faces increasing threats as a result of global warming.
- Bangladesh has to adapt to global warming, and there are a number of options it could adopt.

Unit outcomes

By the end of this unit most students should be able to:
- describe the factors that mean Bangladesh is at risk from flooding;
- describe the threats Bangladesh faces from global warming;
- identify the advantages and barriers in the way of some solutions that Bangladesh could adopt to adapt to global warming.

Ideas for a starter

1 Show students a map of Bangladesh. What do they know about the country? Why is at risk?
2 Show students photos of Bangladesh under water – e.g. use images from the flooding in 2007. Why is this situation likely to increase? Ensure that students are aware that the causes of flooding may be different – i.e. in future the threat of flooding in coastal areas could be as a result of sea level rise caused by global warming.

Ideas for plenaries

1 Use the 'What do you think?' on page 61 of the Student Book as a plenary. Refer back to Unit 1.1. In Kiribati more and more people are leaving each year – becoming the world's first environmental refugees. Does the population of Bangladesh face the same fate?
2 'Over to you' activity 2 could be used as a class discussion to think about how far different countries and organisations would be prepared to help Bangladesh.
3 Summarise what you have learned today in 40 words.

The unit in brief

Indonesia is one of the world's most hazardous countries. Situated on the Pacific Ring of Fire, it experiences earthquakes and volcanic eruptions, plus two monsoon seasons a year, and during El Niño the country suffers from drought. Hazard management is made difficult because of the number and range of natural hazards the country faces. Its struggling economy and political instability worsens the situation. Now Indonesia also faces threats from global warming.

Key ideas

- Indonesia is one of the world's most hazardous countries.
- Indonesia was the country worst affected by the Boxing Day tsunami.
- A new tsunami early warning system has started to be installed in the Indian Ocean (funded by international aid).
- Indonesia's economic and political situation means it struggles to deal with the number and range of natural hazards that it faces.
- Indonesia faces further threats from global warming.

Unit outcomes

By the end of this unit most students should be able to:
- describe the hazards that Indonesia faces;
- explain why Indonesia was the country worst affected by the Boxing Day tsunami;
- classify the reasons why Indonesia finds it difficult to manage its response to hazards;
- describe the threats that Indonesia faces from global warming.

Ideas for a starter

1 Show a video clip of the Boxing Day tsunami and its effect on Indonesia. Why was Indonesia so badly affected?
2 Show students a map of plate boundaries. Locate Indonesia. Ask: How does this explain some of the hazards that Indonesia faces?
3 The 1883 eruption of Krakatau was one of the deadliest volcanic eruptions. Find an account of the eruption and read it to the class.

Ideas for plenaries

1 Use 'Over to you' activity **3** as a plenary.
2 The new tsunami early warning system that started to be installed in the Indian Ocean in 2006 was funded by international aid. Use the 'What do you think?' on page 62 of the Student Book to explore the idea that other countries should help to protect those that face major hazards.
3 Ask students to work in pairs to write a paragraph explaining how hazardous Indonesia is.

2 Going global

Chapter outline

Use this chapter outline and the introductory page of the chapter in the Student Book to give students a mental roadmap for the chapter.

2.1 **Taking the Mickey to the world?** How Disney has become a major player in the global economy

2.2 **What is globalisation?** What globalisation means

2.3 **Getting connected: colonialism** The origins of global connections and how globalisation began

2.4 **Global differences** Whether globalisation reduces global differences

2.5 **Staying connected: global groupings** How different global groupings control economic development

2.6 **Strained connections** Why Africa has not benefited from global connections

2.7 **Corporate connections** The role played by TNCs in the globalisation process

2.8 **Global remix: winners and losers** The emergence of China and India as global players

2.9 **World on the move** The link between globalisation and international movements of people and information

2.10 **Migration into Spain** About migration into Spain and the reasons for it

2.11 **Causes and consequences of European migration** The reasons for, and consequences of, migrant flows within the EU

2.12 **Analysing population change in the UK** Recent changes to the UK's population

2.13 **Megacities: Los Angeles** The rise of the megacity, and whether places as large as Los Angeles can be sustainable

2.14 **Megacities: Mumbai** The rapid changes taking place in Mumbai, and whether India's largest city can also be a global city

2.15 **Environmental consequences of globalisation** How globalisation can contribute to the destruction of the environment

2.16 **Social consequences of globalisation** Some of the social consequences of globalisation

2.17 **Managing change for a better world** Whether globalisation has increased our ecological footprint, and how we can reduce the environmental and social costs of globalisation

About the topic

- Globalisation is happening ever more rapidly.
- Globalisation impacts on the economy, society, and the environment.
- Many argue it is creating an unfair world where the world's poorest people remain poorly connected to the wider world.
- Increasing population migration challenges individuals, communities, and governments.
- Sustainable approaches are needed to meet the challenges of globalisation.

About the chapter

- This chapter uses case studies to show how globalisation occurs, how it has arisen, and its impacts.
- It looks at the origins of global connections and how globalisation began, different global groupings, and Africa's inability to 'connect' with the rest of the world.
- It investigates TNCs, the emergence of China and India as global players, migration into Spain and the EU, and population change in the UK.
- The growth of the megacities uses Los Angeles and Mumbai as case studies, and the chapter ends by looking at the environmental and social consequences of globalisation and how we can reduce these.

Key vocabulary

There is no set list of words in the specification that students must know. However, examiners will use some or all of the following words in the examinations, and would expect students to know them and use them in their answers.

ageing population
Agenda 21
baby booms
carbon sink
centrally planned economies
reverse colonialism
connections, connected, disconnected
core and periphery
deindustrialisation
digital divide
dynamic system
ecological footprint
economic migrants
edge city
enclaves
ethnic enclave
export processing zones
Fair Trade
fertility rate
first, third world
Fortress Europe
free trade

globalisation
grey pound
greying
host nations
hyper-urbanisation
illegal migrant
IMF
immigration
informal sector
inputs and outputs
just-in-time
megacity
megalopolis
immigration
millennium development goals
modernisation theory
natural increase and decrease
net migration
new economy
outsourcing
periphery
population structure
privatisation

pull and push factors
quota
remittances
replacement level
replacement migration
rural-urban migration
Seasonal Agricultural Workers Scheme (SAWS)
seasonal workers
sheltered accommodation
social cohesion
source nations
structural adjustment packages
super city
sustainable development
tariff
three Ds
Total Fertility Rate (TFR)
tourist enclave
trading blocs
urbanisation
World Bank
world city

The glossary at the end of this book contains many of these words and phrases. For students, the key word boxes in the chapter or the glossary at the end of the Student Book will help them with the meanings of all.

The unit in brief

This 2-page unit uses Disney to introduce globalisation. Disney has grown from a small animation studio in California in the 1950s to become a major player in the global economy. The Disney Corporation is involved in many global activities and influences urban planning, media, and governments.

Key ideas

- TNCs play a large part in the global economy.
- Disney is the third-largest global brand (behind Coca Cola and McDonald's).
- The Disney Corporation is involved in many global activities.
- Companies grow by expansion, merger, or takeover, and by diversifying.
- Disney is typical of the new economy (where companies and countries are based more on creativity, in finance, media, and management, rather than on the production of goods).
- Disney's influence is global – it influences urban planning, media, and governments.

Unit outcomes

By the end of this unit most students should be able to:
- locate on a world map where Disney's decisions are made, where goods are produced, where products are consumed, where governments are influenced;
- describe how companies grow;
- explain what the term the 'new economy' means for those in wealthy countries and those in poorer countries;
- describe how Disney influences urban planning, the media, and governments.

Ideas for a starter

1 What do you know about Disney? Write answers on the board as a spider diagram. Then ask: What has Disney got to do with geography?

2 Who are the world's top global brands? (Disney comes third behind Coca Cola and McDonald's.)

Ideas for plenaries

1 Use 'Over to you' activity **3** as a discussion. Get students to write a 350-word report following the discussion, summing up how far Disney is a truly global company.

2 If you used starter **1** return to the spider diagram and add to or modify it.

3 The text on page 67 of the Student Book tells us that before it closed workers in a Bangladesh textile factory were paid 15 cents for every $17.99 Disney shirt they sewed. Use the 'What do you think?' on page 67 to discuss the issue of low wages.

4 Make a graffiti wall of what students have learned today.

The unit in brief

In this 2-page unit students find out what globalisation means. The unit includes examples to show how our world is shrinking. It explains the impacts globalisation has on finance, politics, people, and culture. Those for globalisation think that it brings people together and that trade spreads wealth more equally across the world. Those against it think that existing inequalities will be made worse and there will be more winners and losers.

Key ideas

- While physical distances around the world have remained the same, the time it takes to pass information globally has reduced dramatically.
- Globalisation means the process by which people, their cultures, money, goods, and information can be transferred between countries with few or no barriers.
- Globalisation has impacts on finance, politics, people, and culture.
- The world consists of countries with economic influence, the new manufacturing nations, and the 'have-nots' who have little economic influence.
- There are arguments for and against globalisation.

Unit outcomes

By the end of this unit most students should be able to:
- define globalisation and be able to identify and understand some of its characteristics;
- draw a spider diagram to show the impact globalisation has on finance, politics, people, and culture.
- Identify those who can be seen as the main winners and losers of globalisation, and why;
- identify the gains and losses of globalisation for the individual, the local area, and the UK as globalisation progresses.

Ideas for a starter

1 Read out the paragraph beginning 'Imagine a British tourist …'. Ask students to label the countries mentioned on a blank map of the world. Ask: What is this evidence of?
2 Show students the photo of the Hong Kong street on page 68 of the Student Book. What other global brands, or companies, would they expect to see there? What does this tell them?
3 Hold up an electronic gadget. Ask: Who made it? Where? What does it cost? Who gets most of that money? How does this show evidence of globalisation?

Ideas for plenaries

1 Use 'Over to you' activity **4** as a plenary.
2 Where do you think the clothes you are wearing today were made? Students could check any easily accessible labels. The chances are they will have been made in Asia.
3 Take 2 minutes with a partner and think up one interesting question about globalisation that we have not covered today.

Getting connected: colonialism

The unit in brief

This 4-page unit explores the origins of global connections and how globalisation began. Today's patterns of wealth, trade, and development have been shaped by what has happened in the past and in particular by early colonialism. The unit includes a Background box which explains core and periphery theory – the process by which some countries become wealthy and others poor. The unit also explores how some nations become economically disconnected, and modernisation theory.

Key ideas

- Today's patterns of wealth, trade, and development have been shaped by the past.
- A wealthy core and periphery developed as a result of colonialism.
- The core is where most wealth is produced, while the poorer periphery is usually distant from the core markets.
- As countries become disconnected they are less influential and less involved in economic decision-making.
- Modernisation theory is the process of investment and influence used to develop some parts of the world economically, using Western (mainly American) investment aimed at reducing poverty.

Unit outcomes

By the end of this unit most students should be able to:
- define the terms connections, disconnected, core and periphery, modernisation theory;
- understand how today's patterns of wealth, trade, and development have been shaped by the past;
- explain how colonialism caused the development of a wealthy core and periphery;
- summarise the impacts of colonialism for disconnected nations;
- explain how American aid led to economic development through the philosophy of 'modernisation'.

Ideas for a starter

1 Show students the photo of Mexico City on page 70 of the Student Book (or a similar image). Ask a student to read out the description of Tenochtitlan (the site of the future Mexico City) written by Bernal Diaz. What is the link?
2 Show students an image of Columbus. Ask: When did Columbus land in America? What is the link between Columbus and modern patterns of trade and development?

Ideas for plenaries

1 Ask students to add the terms connections, disconnected, core and periphery theory, and modernisation theory to a dictionary of key terms for 'Going global'.
2 Use the 'What do you think?' of page 73 of the Student Book to get students thinking about what they have learned in this unit.
3 Write the words 'global connections' in the middle of your page. Create a mind map around the phrase. How many ideas can you come up with in 3 minutes.
4 Repeat 3, but for 'global disconnections'.

The unit in brief

This 2-page unit looks at whether globalisation reduces global differences. It investigates differences around the world from the origins of the 'third world' during the Cold War to the classification of countries according to income levels today. It looks at how development is measured using economic and human development indicators, and at trends in human development.

Key ideas

- The term 'third world' originated during the Cold War.
- Although identified as one area, the third world had wide variations within it.
- In 1980 the Brandt Report used a wide range of criteria for judging development.
- Countries are now better classified according to their levels of income as High, Middle, and Low.
- There are enormous differences between the North (developed core) and the South (developing periphery).
- Development can be measured using a range of economic and human development indicators.
- Almost all world regions have increased their HDI score in the last 30 years with the exception of Sub-Saharan Africa.

Unit outcomes

By the end of this unit most students should be able to:
- describe how differences around the world have been described or classified since the Cold War;
- describe five key differences between the North (developed core) and South (developing periphery);
- give three examples of economic indicators and three examples of human development indicators;
- explain why Sub-Saharan Africa has not improved its HDI score;
- decide whether globalisation is reducing global differences, and explain why.

Ideas for a starter

1 Ask students: Who can remember how we measure development? What indicators can we use?
2 What terms do you know for describing the world in terms of development? You are looking for 'rich north', 'poor south' 'developed', developing' etc. How useful are these terms?

Ideas for plenaries

1 Use the 'What do you think?' on page 75 of the Student Book as a plenary. You may get responses similar to the points students raise in starter **2**.
2 Ask: Why has Sub-Saharan Africa not improved its HDI?
3 What was the single most important thing you learned today?

The unit in brief

This is a 2-page unit which looks at how different global groupings control economic development. It begins with the story of a rice farmer in Senegal whose future is uncertain because of unfair trade rules. It considers how global trade is dominated by North America, Europe, and East Asia; the growing importance of China and India, trading blocs, and other trade organisations ranging from the WTO to G20.

Key ideas

- World trade is dominated by three regions: North America; Europe; East Asia.
- India and China are becoming major economic forces.
- Trading blocs group together countries in geographical areas and encourage trade within the bloc (and region).
- There is a range of organisations which exist to promote different types of trade to and from different countries.
- Understand that trade patterns and trading blocs bring benefits and disadvantages to different people.

Unit outcomes

By the end of this unit most students should be able to:
- understand that world trade is dominated by North America, Europe, and East Asia;
- explain how India and China are becoming major economic forces;
- identify the similarities and differences between different trading blocs;
- give five examples of other organisations which promote trade, and say what they do;
- draw a diagram to show how different organisations and groups affect the economic fate of the rice farmer in this unit.

Ideas for a starter

1 Read aloud Mamadou Niang's story from page 76 of the Student Book to set the scene for the unit. Ask students to identify those who influence Mamadou's life whilst you are reading. Discuss what they identify.

2 Show students the map of trading blocs on page 77 minus the key. Ask if anyone can identify the trade blocs. Then ask what trade blocs are. Who do they benefit?

Ideas for plenaries

1 Use the 'What do you think?' on page 77 of the Student Book as a plenary.

2 Create an acrostic. Write GLOBAL GROUPINGS down one side of the page. Make each letter the first letter of a word, phrase, or sentence about global groupings.

3 Go to the World Trade Organisation website (www.wto.org/). Download the principles for the trading system. Put these on the board. Do students agree with them?

The unit in brief

This is a 4-page unit which looks at why Africa has not benefited from global connections. Africa remains disconnected for one simple reason – debt. The unit explains how the world's poorest countries got into debt and includes a Background box which looks at why Africa has failed to make economic progress. Case studies investigate the situation in Zambia, Tanzania, and Kenya, and ask questions about Africa's inability to 'connect' with the rest of the world.

Key ideas

- Africa remains disconnected from the world economy largely because of debt.
- Most debts date from the 1970s.
- Many African countries now use over 40% of their annual incomes to repay loans.
- Africa has made little economic progress over the last 50 years.
- African trade is characterised by exports of primary products, and imports of manufactured goods.
- Some of Africa's problems stem from falls in the value of primary products (e.g. copper and cotton) and the need to grow cash crops to earn money to repay debts.

Unit outcomes

By the end of this unit most students should be able to:
- understand why debt means that Africa has not benefited from global connections;
- explain how African countries got into debt, and the players in this process;
- draw up a table to show the economic, social, and environmental impacts of events in Africa over the past 50 years;
- assess whether a lack of resources, poor quality farmland, and lack of food help to explain Africa's slow rate of development.

Ideas for a starter

1 Put students into 5 equal-size groups. Allocate one of the 5 text boxes to the right of the map on page 78 of the Student Book to each group. Ask them to read it through, and explain in a diagram what they think a) it means and b) are its impacts. Ask them to present their ideas to the rest of the class.

2 Use the text box at the top of page 79 to draw a flow chart showing how the world's poorest countries got into debt. Ask students what they know about OPEC's actions in the 1970s; loans for infrastructure projects; debt etc.

Ideas for plenaries

1 Many African countries are heavily in debt. Use the 'What do you think?' on page 81 of the Student Book to generate a discussion on debt cancellation.

2 How did African countries get into debt?

3 What is Africa's future? Will Africa always remain disconnected?

4 Did you find anything difficult about the work in this unit? What? What would help to make it less difficult?

The unit in brief

This unit explores the role TNCs play in the globalisation process. It lists the top ten TNCs and explains how TNCs grow. It looks at how some supermarkets have become so large that they now act like superpowers and are subject to major criticisms. The unit includes the supermarkets' response to some of the criticisms. It explains how the bigger the supermarket is, the stronger its purchasing power, which increases its ability to control suppliers and prices. A case study of Almeria in Spain shows how Almeria's climate is ideal for growing fruit and vegetables year-round, which is something that the supermarkets demand, but that the system used has serious environmental impacts.

Key ideas

- The top 200 TNCs account for 25% of the world's economic activity.
- TNCs grow as a result of motive, means, and mobility.
- Global supermarket companies control huge volumes of food and non-food goods.
- Supermarkets and other major companies are subject to criticism.
- Growing crops year-round in Almeria for consumers elsewhere in Europe has serious environmental impacts.

Unit outcomes

By the end of this unit most students should be able to:
- list five examples of resource-based, producing, manufacturing, retail, and services TNCs;
- explain how TNCs grow;
- know that supermarkets are seen as contentious, but understand the reasons on both sides of the argument;
- describe the environmental impacts of growing crops under plastic in Almeria.

Ideas for a starter

1 Show the statement in the text box on page 83 of the Student Book on the board. Read it out. Ask students to unpick it. What does it really mean?
2 Ask: Who can name 10 TNCs? What do they do?
3 Show students the photo on page 85. What is the connection between this and TNCs?

Ideas for plenaries

1 Use the 'What do you think?' on page 85 of the Student Book as a plenary.
2 Look at the table at the top of page 84. Ask one group of students to come up with any other criticisms they can think of. Another group of student should act as the supermarkets and respond to the criticisms.
3 Play 'Just a minute'. The topic is transnational corporations. Students have one minute to talk on the topic without repetition or hesitation. If they repeat themselves or hesitate another student takes over.

Global remix: winners and losers

The unit in brief

This is a 6-page unit which investigates the emergence of China and India as global players. China has the world's fastest growing economy and the unit includes a Background box which looks at how China has grown so quickly. The shift to an urban economy has seen the largest rural-urban migration ever recorded. There are many social, economic, and environmental consequences of China's growth. India is the other rapidly emerging superpower and the last spread in this unit looks at India today and how the global balance of trade and power is shifting.

Key ideas

- China and India are countries which have been 'switched on' and are the world's emerging superpowers.
- China's economy has doubled every eight years since the 1970s. In India economic growth has averaged 6% a year since the 1990s.
- China's urban population is rising rapidly.
- There are consequences of China's and India's growth.
- China has grown as a result of manufacturing. India's growth is based on services.
- The global balance of trade and power is shifting.

Unit outcomes

By the end of this unit most students should be able to:
- understand that there have been huge economic shifts in the last twenty years as some countries have become 'switched on';
- explain how China's economy has grown so quickly;
- describe the reasons for the growth in China's urban population;
- classify the consequences of China's growth as social, economic, and environmental;
- describe the reasons for India's economic growth;
- describe how the balance of trade and power is shifting.

Ideas for a starter

1 Show students the photos of Shanghai on page 87 of the Student Book and Bangalore on page 90. Ask: Where are these places? What do you know about them? What do you know about China and India's economies?
2 What are the BRICs? Why are they important?
3 Show the photo of the Emma Maersk on page 86 on the board. Ask a student to read out the list of what the ship was carrying. Where had it come from? Why is this important?

Ideas for plenaries

1 Use 'On your own' activity **8** on page 91 of the Student Book as a plenary.
2 The 'What do you think?' on page 90 could be used to generate a discussion of the costs of China and India's economic growth.
3 Get students to work together to write a paragraph on China's growth.

The unit in brief

This is a 2-page unit which explores the links between globalisation and international movements of people and information. Migration is at an all-time high. In 2006, 3% of the world's population was on the move. This unit looks at who is moving and the impacts this has on both host and source nations. It also looks at how places that are well-connected in terms of communications experience the full impacts of globalisation whilst those that are poorly connected remain 'switched off'.

Key ideas

- Migration has increased due to economic globalisation.
- There are distinct geographical variations in migration patterns.
- Educated and professional people are more likely to move than poorer people.
- Migration has impacts on both host and source nations.
- Communications networks bring places and people closer together, but not everywhere is well-connected.

Unit outcomes

By the end of this unit most students should be able to:
- describe how and why migration has increased since 1960;
- describe the geographical variations in migration patterns;
- explain why educated and professional people are more likely to move than poorer people;
- draw a diagram to show the impacts of migration on host and source nations;
- draw a spider diagram to show how and why modern communications technology 'switches on' and 'switches off' different parts of the world.

Ideas for a starter

1 Show students the map on page 92 of the Student Book. Ask: why do people migrate? Who migrates? What impacts does migration have?
2 Show students the pie chart of internet users on page 93. Ask students to describe what the pie chart shows. What impacts will the lack of internet users have for countries in Africa and the Middle East?

Ideas for plenaries

1 With books closed, ask students to define the terms: international migration, source nation, host nation, remittances, brain drain, digital divide. Now ask them to add them to their dictionary of key terms for 'Going global'.
2 Use the 'What do you think?' on page 93 of the Student Book as a plenary.
3 Tell your neighbour the two key things you learned today.

The unit in brief

This is a 2-page unit which looks at migration into Spain. Spain's population is growing at a rate of around 2% a year, mainly as a result of immigration. Immigration creates benefits for the Spanish economy. The largest group of immigrants come from Morocco followed by those from South America. Others come from within, and outside, the EU. There are large concentrations of retired immigrants in coastal regions, but this has created social and environmental problems.

Key ideas

- Spain's population is growing at around 2% per year, largely as a result of immigration.
- Immigration has economic benefits for Spain.
- Spain's migrants come from Morocco, South America, and the EU.
- Migrants from non-EU countries are accepted as members of the Seasonal Agricultural Workers Scheme.
- Concentrations of retired immigrants in coastal regions has created social and environmental concerns.

Unit outcomes

By the end of this unit most students should be able to:
- explain the reason for Spain's population growth;
- understand why Spain encourages immigration;
- describe the pattern of migration into Spain;
- complete a table showing the problems migration causes for Spain.

Ideas for a starter

1 Who can remind me what these terms mean: natural increase, immigration, ageing population, fertility rate, enclave?
2 Show students a population pyramid for Spain (like the one on page 94 of the Student Book, but minus the outline for foreigners). Ask them to describe the population structure. Can this type of population structure cause problems?

Ideas for plenaries

1 If you want to hold a class discussion then use either 'Over to you' activity **3** or the 'What do you think?' on page 95 of the Student Book.
2 What are the benefits for Spain of immigration? What problems does it cause?
3 Sum up what you have learned today in 35 words.

The unit in brief

This 6-page unit examines the reasons for, and consequences of, migrant flows within the EU. It starts by looking at changing migration patterns and the impact that EU enlargement has had on migration. It explores why people move (push and pull factors), why migrants are needed, and the opportunities created by migration. It also looks at the challenges that immigration causes. The final spread tackles illegal immigration and exploitation. It ends by explaining that EU governments face the challenge of maintaining social cohesion while still encouraging immigration.

Key ideas

- Migration patterns into the UK have changed as a result of EU enlargement.
- Most migrants are economic migrants.
- Migrants move as a result of push and pull factors.
- Replacement migration is where migrant workers are encouraged to move from EU member states which have a labour surplus to those with labour or skills shortages.
- Immigration creates social and cultural challenges.
- There has been a sharp rise in the number of people trying to enter the EU illegally.
- Many illegal immigrants (along with some legal ones) suffer from exploitation.

Unit outcomes

By the end of this unit most students should be able to:
- explain how migration patterns into the UK have changed;
- produce a poster of the push and pull factors that explain migration from countries such as Poland, Latvia, and Romania into the UK;
- explain why replacement migration can benefit host and source countries;
- explain why social cohesion is a major challenge facing EU governments in relation to immigration;
- describe the routes illegal immigrants use to enter Europe;
- describe and suggest reasons for the pattern of population change in Europe;
- explain the link between the informal sector and exploitation.

Ideas for a starter

1 Show students the table on page 96 of the Student Book. How has the pattern of immigration into the UK changed? Why?
2 Show students clips from the film *Ghost* about the Morecombe Bay cockle pickers. It is a vivid demonstration of the lengths some people go to, to enter the UK illegally, and the exploitation that they face.

Ideas for plenaries

1 You could use starter **2** as a plenary if you have not already used it.
2 Remind students that migration can have a major impact on population change. Show the map and scattergraph on page 99 of the Student Book and ask them to describe the patterns shown.
3 Write the phrase 'Causes and consequences of European migration' in the middle of your page. Create a mind map around the phrase.

The unit in brief

In this 8-page unit students learn abut the recent changes to the UK's population. It begins by looking at the factors that influence population change and the fact that the UK has an ageing population. It explains the reasons for the baby booms that the UK experienced in the twentieth century and looks at changes in fertility. It looks at the impact of migration on the age structure of the UK using some well-known celebrities as examples and finally considers the issues facing society as the UK's population changes. The final spread also tells students how they can investigate their local population.

Key ideas

- The factors that influence population change can be divided into social, cultural, political, economic, and demographic.
- The UK's population is ageing and this creates challenges and opportunities.
- The UK experienced four baby booms in the twentieth century.
- Fertility rates in most European countries have dropped below the replacement level.
- Since the 1980s net immigration has contributed a higher percentage of the UK's population growth than natural increase.
- Ethnic population groups in the UK have a different age structure to the white British population.

Unit outcomes

By the end of this unit most students should be able to:
- describe and explain how social, cultural, political, economic, and demographic factors influence population change;
- explain why life expectancy is increasing in the UK and describe the challenges and opportunities that this creates;
- explain how the birth rate in the UK is influenced by political, social, and economic factors;
- define replacement level and describe changes in European fertility rates;
- explain the impact of migration on the UK's population;
- explain the differences in the age structures of different ethnic groups in the UK.

Ideas for a starter

1 Show students the graph of completion of new houses in the UK on page 109 of the Student Book. Ask: What does this tell us about population change?
2 Show students the photos on age 107. What impact has immigration had on the UK's population growth? Do different ethnic population groups have the same age structure?
3 What are the age structures of families in the class? How old are the oldest members? Has life expectancy increased in students' families?

Ideas for plenaries

1 Ask students to define the terms population structure, greying population, baby boom, total fertility rate, replacement level. Then get them to add them to their dictionary of key terms for this chapter.
2 Ask students to work together to write a paragraph on the issues facing society as the UK's population ages.

The unit in brief

This 6-page unit uses Los Angeles as a case study of a megacity. It begins by looking at urbanisation and the growth of the megacities and then goes on to look at how Los Angeles grew. Like many large urban areas, Los Angeles has a number of problems – and its biggest one is suburban sprawl and the related problem of pollution. The unit looks at land use in Los Angeles and why it has been described as a 'donut' city. It ends by asking whether Los Angeles can be sustainable.

Key ideas

- Urbanisation is increasing and megacities are also growing.
- Los Angeles is a world city with connections to other cities around the world.
- Los Angeles grew for specific reasons and is still growing.
- The biggest problems faced by Los Angeles are suburban sprawl and pollution.
- Los Angeles has been described as a 'donut' city.
- Land use patterns in Los Angeles do not conform to a typical land use model.
- The Progressive Los Angeles Network (PLAN) proposes an agenda for sustainable living.

Unit outcomes

By the end of this unit most students should be able to:
- describe the distribution of the world's megacities;
- describe the reasons for Los Angeles' growth;
- classify the impacts of suburbanisation as social, economic, and environmental;
- explain why Los Angeles has been described as a 'donut' city;
- explain how ethnic enclaves complicate the land use pattern in Los Angeles;
- give six examples of PLAN's proposals for a sustainable city.

Ideas for a starter

1 Show students a photos of Los Angeles (positive images e.g. good quality housing, low density etc.). Ask a student to read out the quote on page 110 of the Student Book. Ask: Is this the American Dream? Is it like this for everyone? Or is the reality rather different?
2 Brainstorm: What images does the name Los Angeles conjure up? Record students' responses.

Ideas for plenaries

1 If you used starter **2** revisit the responses recorded. Do you need to add to/amend anything as a result of what students have learned in this unit?
2 'Over to you' activity **2** could be used as a plenary.
3 Use the 'What do you think?' on page 115 of the Student Book to discuss sustainability in megacities.
4 Ask students to add the key vocabulary from this unit to their dictionary of key terms for 'Going global'.

The unit in brief

This is the second unit looking at megacities. This 6-page one uses Mumbai as a case study in contrast to Los Angeles in Unit 2.13. Mumbai is the commercial capital of India and a city of distinct contrasts. It is experiencing hyper-urbanisation as a result of rural-urban migration. Many migrants end up living in places like Dharavi, one of the world's largest shanty towns. *Vision Mumbai* is Mumbai's plan to tackle its problems and transform the city. But part of the plan involves demolishing slums like Dharavi, and that is contentious. If *Vision Mumbai* is not successful, then Mumbai may not become the global city it wants to be.

Key ideas

- The growth of Mumbai and India has brought wealth and power to some people, but not all.
- Mumbai is experiencing hyper-urbanisation as a result of rural-urban migration.
- 60% of Mumbai's population live in poverty in places like Dharavi.
- Dharavi can support itself and is sustainable.
- *Vision Mumbai* is a plan to tackle the problems of a slow-down in economic growth and deterioration in quality of life.
- *Vision Mumbai* is based on six core targets.
- Mumbai's future success is in the balance.

Unit outcomes

By the end of this unit most students should be able to:
- understand that Mumbai's growth has not benefited everyone;
- draw a diagram to explain the problems created by rural-urban migration and hyper-urbanisation;
- describe how Dharavi is sustainable;
- describe how *Vision Mumbai* will tackle Mumbai's problems and name the six core targets;
- explain why Mumbai's future success is in the balance.

Ideas for a starter

1 Show students the two photos on page 116 of the Student Book. Ask them to describe what they show. Who lives in the slums? Why? What must life be like?
2 Read out to the class the text 'Two cities – dual societies'. Use it to set the scene for this unit.

Ideas for plenaries

1 Use the 'What do you think?' on page 121 of the Student Book to generate a discussion. Ask students to put themselves in the shoes of someone who lives in Dharavi. Is *Vision Mumbai* good news for everyone?
2 Show students the photo on page 121 of Mumbai's over-crowded trains. How could this issue derail Mumbai's chances of becoming the next Shanghai?
3 Think back over this unit and write down three questions related to what you have learned. The teacher will ask a member of the class to try to answer.

The unit in brief

This 2-page unit looks at how globalisation can contribute to the destruction of the environment. It considers deforestation and the links between deforestation, debt, and trade. It looks at the impact deforestation has on climate change and some of the other environmental costs of globalisation and economic growth.

Key ideas

- Deforestation, economic growth, trade, and debt are all linked.
- 'Debt for nature swaps' are one way of tackling the debt and deforestation issue.
- Deforestation has major impacts on climate change.
- Economic growth and resource use raises serious issues.

Unit outcomes

By the end of this unit most students should be able to:
- draw a diagram to show the links between deforestation, economic growth, trade, and debt;
- describe how 'debt for nature' swaps work;
- describe the impacts deforestation has on climate change;
- identify the issues raised by economic growth and resource use.

Ideas for a starter

1 Write two words on the board – 'globalisation' and 'deforestation'. Ask students: What is the link between them?
2 Show students the image of the burning rainforest in Brazil on page 122 of the Student Book (or any similar image). Ask: What are the environmental consequences of this?

Ideas for plenaries

1 With books closed ask students to define these terms taken from the text: deforestation, biodiversity, debt for nature swaps, carbon sink. Then get them to add them to their dictionary of key terms for this chapter.
2 Use the 'What do you think?' on page 123 of the Student Book for a discussion on the environmental consequences of globalisation.
3 Sum up what you have learned today in 35 words.

The unit in brief

This 2-page unit looks at some of the social and moral consequences of globalisation, using tourism in Cuba as a case study. Tourism is the world's biggest industry. It is a global business linking companies in different countries, and they all want to make a profit. In Cuba tourism now supports economic development, but Cuba is changing as a result of globalisation.

Key ideas

- Tourism is a major driving force behind globalisation.
- Cuba is an example of a country switching into the global economy.
- Income from tourism supports economic development in Cuba.
- There are social and moral consequences of tourism in Cuba.

Unit outcomes

By the end of this unit most students should be able to:
- explain how and why tourism is a major driving force behind globalisation;
- describe how Cuba has switched into the global economy;
- explain how tourism supports economic development in Cuba;
- draw up a list of the social and moral consequences of tourism in Cuba and identify who benefits and who loses out.

Ideas for a starter

1 Show students three photos: one of Fidel Castro, one of a hotel in Cuba, and one of an aeroplane. Ask: What is the link between these photos and globalisation?
2 Use 'Over to you' activity 1 as a starter to get students thinking about the consequences of tourism.
3 Ask: What do we mean by the term 'social consequences'?

Ideas for plenaries

1 What do these terms mean: repatriation of profits, tourist enclave?
2 Use 'On your own' activity 5 as a plenary.
3 Use the 'What do you think?' on page 125 of the Student Book to generate a discussion on the social costs of globalisation.
4 What was the most important insight you gained from this unit?

The unit in brief

This final 4-page unit of 'Going global' considers how we are living beyond our environmental means and how we can reduce some of the social and environmental costs of globalisation. The UK is the world's second largest consumer of natural resources and goods – only the USA consumes more than us. The unit compares the ecological footprint of countries at different stages of development. It examines how people have woken up to global issues and the challenge of sustainable development. The second spread of this unit looks at some of the challenges we face as we try to reduce the social and environmental costs of globalisation.

Key ideas

- The UK has the world's second largest ecological footprint.
- As people have increased access to technology they become more aware of global issues.
- Globalisation and sustainable development need to exist side-by-side.
- We face a number of challenges to reduce the social and environmental costs of globalisation and make the world a better place.

Unit outcomes

By the end of this unit most students should be able to:
- define ecological footprint and explain why less developed countries have smaller footprints than more developed countries;
- give five examples of events that have raised the global conscience;
- choose one event, find out about the issues it dealt with, and what has happened since;
- outline the four challenges we face to reduce the social and environmental costs of globalisation;
- explain why some countries will find it easier to meet the challenges than others.

Ideas for a starter

1 Show students the table on page 126 of the Student Book. Do the figures surprise them? Did they expect the UK to be so high up the table? Why do less developed countries have smaller footprints?
2 Show students the photo on page 128. Ask: What has this got to do with globalisation?
3 Who can tell me what 'ecological footprint' means? Who knows what Agenda 21 is? Why is it important?

Ideas for plenaries

1 Can individuals make a difference to the impacts of globalisation? Use the 'What do you think?' on page 128 of the Student Book as the basis for a discussion.
2 Ask: Who would be prepared to pay more for certain goods if the extra money benefited the growers and farmers? So, who buys Fair Trade products? What do they buy?
3 Do an alphabet run for 'Going global', finding a word linked to what has been covered in this chapter for each letter.

3 Extreme weather

Chapter outline

Use this chapter outline and the introductory page of the chapter in the Student Book to give students a mental roadmap for the chapter.

3.1 Extreme heat Europe's heat wave in 2003; anticyclones and synoptic charts

3.2 From one extreme to another Extreme weather around the world, UK weather extremes, and links with climate change

3.3 Increasing the risk How people and places are increasingly vulnerable to extreme weather

3.4 One extreme storm The Boscastle flood in August 2004; impacts and events

3.5 What caused the Boscastle flood? Storms, depressions, satellite images, and hydrographs, plus other ways of increasing the flood risk

3.6 Managing flooding Defending Boscastle, flood forecasting and warning, and protecting places at risk

3.7 Hurricane Katrina, August 2005 What happened when Hurricane Katrina hit New Orleans, how the hurricane developed, and why it was so disastrous

3.8 All about hurricanes How hurricanes develop, where they occur, and how they are measured

3.9 Managing hurricanes How New Orleans' defences are being restored and how people can manage the hurricane risk

3.10 The Big Dry What drought is, and how Australia's first drought of the twenty-first century has affected the country

3.11 What caused the drought? Climate patterns and El Niño, and climate change

3.12 Managing Australia's water How Australia is managing its scarce water resources

3.13 Gloucestershire under water Impacts and causes of the Gloucestershire floods in July 2007, and how Cheltenham manages flooding

About the topic

- Extreme weather includes a range of phenomena which develop from a variety of weather conditions.
- This topic looks at how extreme weather events lead to a range of hazards from the immediate to the longer term.
- Extreme weather has a variety of impacts – social, economic, and environmental.
- People and places are increasingly vulnerable to extreme weather events which seem to be becoming more frequent and severe.
- Extreme weather events and the hazards they cause need managing.

About the chapter

- This chapter tackles the topic of extreme weather through a case study approach backed up with theory where needed.
- It begins with Europe's heat wave in 2003, and includes case studies of the Boscastle flood in 2004, Hurricane Katrina in 2005, the Australian drought which began in 2002, and the flooding in Gloucestershire in 2007.

Key vocabulary

There is no set list of words in the specification that students must know. However, examiners will use some or all of the following words in the examinations, and would expect students to know them and use them in their answers.

air mass	hurricane watch
anticyclone	hydrograph
catchment area	jet stream
cold front	landslides
convergence of air masses	levees
coriolis force	occluded front
deforestation	rising limb
depression	shanty towns
discharge of a river	soft engineering
drought	storm surge
El Niño	trade winds
eye of a hurricane	urbanisation
flood walls	Walker cell
hard engineering	warm front

The glossary at the end of this book contains many of these words and phrases. For students, the key word boxes in the chapter or the glossary at the end of the Student Book will help them with the meanings of all.

The unit in brief

This 2-page unit uses the example of the 2003 heat wave in Europe to introduce students to the idea of extreme weather. The heat wave began in June and continued until mid-August and had some devastating impacts. Over 30 000 people died and over 25 000 forest fires broke out. Extreme weather events develop due to a variety of meteorological conditions and this unit includes background information on anticyclones and synoptic charts. A stationary anticyclone caused the heat wave in 2003.

Key ideas

- Extreme weather includes a range of phenomena that involve extremes of temperature, precipitation, wind and atmospheric pressure.
- Extreme weather causes hazards such as floods, droughts and heat waves.
- The heat wave in 2003 had wide ranging social, environmental and economic impacts.
- Anticyclones are high pressure weather systems. A stationary anticyclone caused the heat wave in 2003.
- Synoptic charts are used to plot weather conditions of certain areas at a single point in time.

Unit outcomes

By the end of this unit most students should be able to:
- understand that extremes of temperature, precipitation, wind and atmospheric pressure causes extreme weather;
- understand that extreme weather causes hazards;
- classify the impacts of heat waves into social, environmental and economic;
- explain how anticyclones can cause heat waves.

Ideas for a starter

1 Show students examples of photos of the impacts of extreme weather events, e.g. forest fires, parched landscapes (drought), floods, effects of hurricanes, blizzards etc. Ask: What do these show? What do they have in common (elicit that they are examples of extreme weather events)? What causes these things (they develop from a range of meteorological conditions that involve extremes of temperature, precipitation, wind and atmospheric pressure)?

2 Write words such as *severe, unexpected, record, extreme* on the whiteboard. Ask: What do these terms mean? How do they relate to weather?

3 Brainstorm extreme weather. What is it? Can you give me some examples? Where does it happen? Who does it affect? What are the impacts?

Ideas for plenaries

1 Get students to start to build a dictionary of key terms to do with extreme weather. Start with the key vocabulary in this unit.

2 Give students a blank map of Europe. Ask them to locate the 2003 heat wave, add the date and three key impacts.

The unit in brief

This 2-page unit looks at some of the evidence that extreme weather hazards are becoming more frequent. The world map shows the global distribution of weather – related disasters (including drought, extreme temperatures, floods, landslides, fires and windstorms) from 2000-2005. Global extremes are matched by extremes in the UK. 2007 was noted for its extremes of rainfall and temperature as the timeline shows. The Intergovernmental Panel on Climate Change (IPCC) is becoming increasingly confident of the links between climate change and the increase in extreme weather events, as the table on page 129 shows.

Key ideas

- Since 2000 extreme weather events have caused tens of thousands of deaths and caused extensive damage.
- In the UK 2007 was noted for its weather extremes.
- Scientists say that it is not possible to link any one extreme weather event to global warming, but there is evidence that certain events are becoming more frequent and more intense.
- The IPCC is becoming more confident of the links between climate change and the increase in extreme weather events.

Unit outcomes

By the end of this unit most students should be able to:
- understand that extreme weather events affect large numbers of people and result in huge amounts of damage both globally and in the UK;
- understand that there is evidence that some extreme weather events have increased in both frequency and intensity;
- recognise that there is a link between climate change and the increase in extreme weather events.

Ideas for a starter

1 Ask students what is the weather like now? Is it extreme in any way? Are any parts of the UK or Europe currently being affected by extreme weather? What was the last period of extreme weather they can recall?
2 Ask: Who can remind what we mean by severe, unexpected, record, or extreme when we are talking about weather?

Ideas for plenaries

1 Provide students with the information to complete 'On your own' **2.**
  You should be able to access the rest of the year's weather from www.bbc.co.uk/weather/ukweather/year_review
2 Summarise what you have learned today in 35 words.
3 What are the likely impacts of an increase in the number of heat waves, and who are the most vulnerable?
  What are the likely impacts on an increased number of heavy rainfall events?

The unit in brief

This unit looks at how people and places are increasingly vulnerable to the impacts of extreme weather. In these 2 pages students investigate how an increasing proportion of the world's population is living less than 10 metres above sea level and near the coast (in the 'at-risk' zone). In addition increasing numbers in both England and Wales, along with the rest of Europe, are living either on floodplains, or in flood-risk areas.

Rapid population growth in LEDCs, along with urbanisation, means huge numbers of people live in shanty towns – often built in dangerous locations vulnerable to mudflows, landslides etc. following heavy rain. Poor land management, such as deforestation, is another factor which leaves people increasingly vulnerable to the effects of extreme weather.

Key ideas

- People and places are increasingly vulnerable to extreme weather.
- Population growth along coasts and on floodplains (or in flood risk areas) makes people vulnerable to the impacts of worsening storms, floods (and also rising sea levels).
- In LEDCs rapid urbanisation means many people live in shanty towns which are vulnerable to heavy rain, mudflows, landslides etc.
- Poor land management, e.g. deforestation can lead to increased run off, risk of flooding, mud and landslides.
- Some people are more vulnerable than others to extreme weather events.

Unit outcomes

By the end of this unit most students should be able to:
- understand that population growth along coasts and on floodplains makes people vulnerable to extreme weather;
- explain why people living in shanty towns are at risk from extreme weather;
- explain the link between debt, deforestation and landslides.

Ideas for a starter

1 Is your school or college at risk from flooding? Do your students live on flooodplains or in other areas that might be at risk from flooding? Use the flood map tool on the Environment Agency website www.environment-agency.gov.uk/ to find out and show students. You and they might not be at risk from flooding, but millions of people are.
2 Show students photos of Dhaka, the Maldives and Vietnam. Ask students 'What have these places got in common?. They are all 'at-risk' – with large numbers of people living either less than 10 metres above sea level or on the coast.

Ideas for plenaries

1 Get students to add the key vocabulary from this unit to their dictionary of key terms to do with extreme weather.
2 Base a plenary on the 'What do you think?' and quote from Professor Bob Spicer on page 130 'Floodplains are called floodplains for a reason – they flood.' Ask the question 'So, why do we build on floodplains?'
3 Ask students to work in pairs to write a paragraph on 'How are places and people increasingly vulnerable to extreme weather?' They will need to refer to Unit 3.2.

The unit in brief

This unit is the start of the case study of the Boscastle flood of 16 August 2004. The flood devastated the Cornish village of Boscastle and was the result of an extreme, but localised storm. These 4 pages start with an OS map extract of the Boscastle area, an eyewitness account and a dramatic photo of the flood as it raged through the village. It investigates the effects of the flood, and gives a blow by blow account of what happened that day from the first rainfall to the time when the flooding began to recede. The unit also includes information on the catchment area and facts and figures about the amount of rainfall and speed of river flow.

Key ideas

- The Boscastle flood was an extreme, though short-lived, event.
- Severe weather and flooding had hit the Boscastle area in the past.
- The flood had a devastating effect on Boscastle's economy. Property, residents, visitors and infrastructure were also affected.
- The catchment area of the Valency and Jordan rivers is small and steep, and the rivers reacted rapidly to the intense heavy rainfall.
- Heavy rainfall began at 12.00 noon. By 5.00 p.m. the floods were at their peak, but by 8.00 p.m. water levels were back within the river banks.

Unit outcomes

By the end of this unit most students should be able to:
- describe the social and economic impacts of the flood;
- use evidence from the OS map to explain why Boscastle flooded so badly;
- describe the sequence of events on 16 August 2004.

Ideas for a starter

1   Show images of the Boscastle flood, either the river in full flow (as in the photo on page 132 of the Student Book) or photos of the aftermath. Ask students to describe the impacts such a flood would have. Keep a list of the impacts for use in plenary 1.
2   Show students the OS map extract of Boscastle – either use the one on page132 of the Student Book or show it on a whiteboard. Ask students to look at and describe the topography of the area, e.g. steep-sided valleys, to get them to start thinking about why the rivers reacted so rapidly to the intense rainfall.

Ideas for plenaries

1   If you used starter 1 ask students to classify the list of impacts into social, environmental and economic.
2   Give students a blank map of the UK. Get them to locate Boscastle, add the date of the flood and key impacts.
3   Boscastle has flooded before 2004, and since (in 2007). Other places have flooded more than once. Use the 'What do you think' on page 135 to get students to start thinking critically about why people continue to live in places that are prone to extreme weather events.

The unit in brief

This is a 4-page unit which continues the focus on the Boscastle flood, and looks at the causes of the flood. A large depression dominated the eastern Atlantic Ocean on 16 August and a string of slow moving thunderstorms grew out of this. They produced intense, but very localised, rainfall along the north Cornwall coast. The intense rainfall, along with the topography of the area, caused the flood. The unit includes background information on the development of depressions and hydrographs, and also includes a synoptic chart and satellite image for 16 August. It ends by looking at how human activity can increase the risk of flooding. Although human activity was considered unlikely to have increased the risk of flooding in Boscastle, in other places urbanisation, farming, diverting rivers and destruction of natural environments all increase the flood risk.

Key ideas

- Localised intense rainfall (produced by storms which grew out of a depression) coupled with the small steep catchment area of the Valency and the Jordan caused the flood.
- There were wide variations in the amount of rain that fell on 16 August.
- Depressions are areas of low atmospheric pressure which form over the Atlantic Ocean when warm air from the tropics meets cold air from polar regions.
- Satellite images show us the cloud cover associated with depressions and anticyclones.
- A flood or storm hydrograph shows how a river responds to one particular storm and shows both rainfall and discharge.
- Human activity can increase the risk of flooding from rivers.

Unit outcomes

By the end of this unit most students should be able to:
- explain what caused the Boscastle flood;
- describe the distribution of rainfall on 16 August;
- explain how a depression develops;
- describe what a flood or storm hydrograph shows;
- explain how human activity can increase the flood risk.

Ideas for a starter

1 Brainstorm the causes of flooding. Create a spider diagram on the board of students' responses. Ask: What do you think caused the Boscastle flood?
2 Ask students: Who can remind me what depressions are? Where do they form? What kind of weather do they bring to the UK?
3 Show students the synoptic chart on page 138 of the Student Book. Ask: What is this? What does it show? Does anyone know what a trough is?

Ideas for plenaries

1 Using a blank flood hydrograph diagram, ask students to label the following: discharge, rainfall, peak rainfall, peak discharge, rising limb, falling limb, lag time, time.
2 Use the 'What do you think?' on page 139 of the Student Book as a plenary to generate a discussion on the effect human activity can have on increasing the flood risk.
3 With books closed ask individual students to explain these terms to the class: convergence, depression, warm front, cold front, occluded front, satellite image, hydrograph, discharge, rising limb, lag time. Then get students to add them to their dictionary of key terms for 'Extreme weather'.

The unit in brief

This unit looks at how we can protect ourselves against the risk of flooding. The first page of this 4-page unit looks at what has been done to help protect Boscastle from future flooding. Although Boscastle flooded again in 2007 the defences already in place by then meant that the river did not burst its banks and flooding was less severe than in 2004.

The remainder of the unit looks at how we can manage the flood risk caused by extreme weather events in terms of the role of various agencies such as the Environment Agency, local authorities, police and fire services; how we can protect places at risk from flooding through hard and soft engineering and how we can protect ourselves by insuring against the flood risk.

Key ideas

- The 2004 Boscastle flood was one of the most extreme experienced in Britain.
- After the 2004 flood a number of new flood defences were planned and due to be completed by 2008.
- The Environment Agency is responsible for flood forecasting and warning. Other agencies, e.g. local authorities, the police and fire services, also help to manage the flood risk.
- Flood defences can consist of either hard engineering or soft engineering.
- Flood defences have to take into account the frequency and extent of flooding, cost and sustainability.
- People can protect their property against flooding by insurance.

Unit outcomes

By the end of this unit most students should be able to:
- describe the flood defences planned for Boscastle after the 2004 flood;
- describe the Environment Agency's role in managing the flood risk;
- give four examples of both hard and soft engineering type flood defences and consider whether they are sustainable;
- understand that although people can insure themselves against flooding the insurance costs are likely to rise.

Ideas for a starter

1 Show students photos of the Boscastle flood. Brainstorm – Could this happen again? What type of flood defences could be put in place to prevent it happening, or to make the flooding less severe?

2 Ask: Who can remind me about hard and soft engineering in terms of flood defence. Can you give me some examples?

Ideas for plenaries

1 Get students to add the terms hard and soft engineering to their dictionary of key terms for 'Extreme weather'.

2 Use the 'What do you think?' on page 143 of the Student Book to spark a discussion on the benefits and disadvantages of hard and soft engineering.

3 Use the OS map extract on page 132 and the lists of hard and soft engineering on page 142. Can you identify any other types of defences which could be used in or around Boscastle? Where could they go?

Hurricane Katrina, August 2005

The unit in brief

This unit is the start of the case study on Hurricane Katrina which devastated New Orleans in August 2005. These 4 pages begin by looking at the impacts that the hurricane had on New Orleans – on the infrastructure and social and economic impacts. The second spread considers why New Orleans suffered so badly from Hurricane Katrina concentrating on its location, the levees and floodwalls (which failed), the wetlands which are disappearing rapidly around New Orleans and asking whether global warming was to blame.

Key ideas

- Hurricane Katrina was the third strongest recorded hurricane to make landfall on the USA.
- Hurricane Katrina had major impacts on infrastructure as well as social and economic impacts.
- Hurricane Katrina began life as a tropical depression but reached category 5 on the Saffir-Simpson scale before weakening to category 3 as it made landfall in Louisiana.
- The main threats from hurricanes are rain, wind and storm surges.
- New Orleans was devastated by Hurricane Katrina because of its location, the failure of some levees and floodwalls, the disappearance of the wetlands.
- Global warming may be the cause of an increase in hurricane intensity.

Unit outcomes

By the end of this unit most students should be able to:
- describe the impacts of Hurricane Katrina on New Orleans;
- explain why rain, wind and storm surges cause major threats from hurricanes;
- explain why New Orleans' location, and the disappearance of the wetlands were key factors in the devastation of New Orleans;
- understand that although global warming may result in increased hurricane intensity it is difficult to be categorical about this.

Ideas for a starter

1 Show images of the devastation caused by Hurricane Katrina, or a video clip of a hurricane in action. Ask students to describe the impacts a hurricane might have. Keep a list of the impacts for use in plenary 1.
2 Ask students where is New Orleans? Ask students to mark it on a blank map of the USA. Annotate the map with any geographical information they know about New Orleans.
3 Find a personal account of a hurricane (ideally Hurricane Katrina) and read it aloud to the class.

Ideas for plenaries

1 If you used starter 1 compare the list of impacts with those on page 144 of the Student Book. Students can add to/amend the list of impacts they came up with.
2 Use the 'What do you think?' on page 147 to spark a debate on why people live in areas at risk from hazards such as hurricanes.
3 'Over to you' activity 2 could be used as a plenary.
4 On a blank map of the USA ask students to add the track of Hurricane Katrina, the date it hit New Orleans and the key impacts.

The unit in brief

This 2-page unit provides students with hurricane theory. It looks at what hurricanes are, how and where they develop and how they are measured.

Key ideas

- Hurricanes are intense, destructive, low-pressure weather systems.
- Hurricanes develop: over warm tropical oceans (sea temperature needs to be at least 27°C); in late summer and early autumn; where there is low atmospheric shear.
- Hurricane formation is not completely understood, but hurricanes require heat to power the storm. When they reach land the source of heat energy and moisture disappear and they rapidly decrease in strength.
- Hurricanes occur in the trade wind belts between latitudes 5° and 20° either side of the equator.
- Hurricanes are measured using the Saffir-Simpson scale which is based on a hurricane's intensity.

Unit outcomes

By the end of this unit most students should be able to:
- describe the conditions needed for hurricanes to develop;
- draw a diagram to help explain how hurricanes form;
- describe where hurricanes occur;
- say how hurricanes are measured, and relate this to wind speed, height of storm surge and damage caused by hurricanes.

Ideas for a starter

1 Ask: Who can remind me about hurricanes? Come up with ten things you know about them.
2 What is the most recent hurricane / typhoon / cyclone to hit the news? Where was it? What category was it? When did it happen? Locate it on the map on page 149 of the Student Book.

Ideas for plenaries

1 Question time! Think back over this unit and write down three questions related to what you have learned. The teacher will ask a member of the class to try to answer.
2 Use 'Over to you' activity 1 as a plenary.
3 Get students to add the key vocabulary for hurricanes to their dictionary of key terms for 'Extreme weather'.

The unit in brief

The 2 pages in this unit look at how New Orleans' defences are being restored and how the hurricane risk can be managed. The restoration of the defences include repairing the existing levees and floodwalls, installing temporary floodgates and pumps plus possibly building weirs to regulate the flow of the Mississippi River Gulf Outlet and high levees to the east and north of the city. *Coast 2050* is a major plan which aims to restore Louisiana's wetlands and help protect places inland. Managing the risk includes hurricane prediction and preparation, as well as attempting to reduce the impact of hurricanes by evacuation.

Key ideas

- New Orleans defences- in terms of levees and floodwalls – are being repaired and strengthened.
- Louisiana's natural wetlands are being restored to help protect places inland.
- Managing the hurricane risk includes:
  - Prediction
  - Preparation
  - Reducing the impact by evacuation

Unit outcomes

By the end of this unit most students should be able to:
- describe how New Orleans' defences were being restored;
- explain the importance of restoring Louisiana's wetlands;
- understand how the hurricane risk can be managed by prediction and preparation;
- understand why evacuation is difficult, and why not everyone can evacuate places at risk from hurricanes.

Ideas for a starter

1 Show images of Louisiana's wetlands (or use the photo on page 147 of the Student Book). Ask: Who can remind me why the wetlands are so special? Can they be restored? Use this to introduce *Coast 2050*.

2 Use the 'What do you think?' on page 151 to introduce the idea of restoring New Orleans defences. New Orleans faces the threat of flooding from the Mississippi, from coastal storms and storm surges and from heavy rain. Perhaps it should just have been abandoned?

Ideas for plenaries

1 What is the difference between a hurricane watch and a hurricane warning?
2 Sum up what you have learned today in 40 words.
3 Add information about how New Orleans' hurricane defences are being repaired and restored to the blank map of the USA used in Unit 3.7.

The unit in brief

This 4-page unit is the start of the case study of Australia's drought. By 2007 Australia was in the grip of its worst drought on record. The drought began in 2002 and the worst affected area was the Murray-Darling Basin which provides 40% of Australia's agricultural produce and provides 75% of Australia's water. Drought is nothing new in Australia and the unit includes an Australian drought fact file. The second spread of this unit looks at the impacts drought has on agriculture (always the first to suffer when drought hits) as well as a range of other social, environmental and economic impacts.

Key ideas

- The drought affecting Australia in 2007 was the worst drought on record.
- The Murray-Darling Basin (the area worst affected by the drought) is critical to Australia in terms of agricultural production and water supply.
- Drought is an acute shortage of water.
- Australia's rainfall pattern is one of the most variable in the world and many areas are subject to the threat of drought.
- In Australia agriculture suffers first and most severely when drought hits.
- Drought causes a wide range of social, environmental and economic impacts.

Unit outcomes

By the end of this unit most students should be able to:
- understand the significance of the Murray-Darling Basin to Australia;
- understand that what constitutes a drought varies from one country to another;
- describe the impacts drought has on agriculture;
- classify the impacts of drought into social, environmental and economic.

Ideas for a starter

1 Read the news item on page 152 of the Student Book about Malcolm Adlington aloud to the class. The Big Dry is a live issue for people like Malcolm and countless others. This item helps to set the scene for the rest of this unit and the case study.
2 Draw an outline of the Murray-Darling Basin on the board. Ask individual students to annotate it with the bulleted points in the text box on page 152.

Ideas for plenaries

1 Use the 'What do you think?' on page 155 of the Student Book. Draw a web of the impacts of drought using the text boxes on pages 154 and 155. Although these are categorised as impacts on agriculture, along with other social, environmental and economic impacts there are clearly links and overlaps between them.
2 Starter 2 or 'Over to you' 1 could be used as a plenary.
3 Create a graffiti wall of what students have learned in this unit.

What caused the drought?

The unit in brief

This unit looks at the possible causes of the drought in Australia. The first two pages investigate climatic variation in the Pacific – what happens in 'normal' years, and then the changes that occur with La Niña and El Niño. El Niño can cause drier conditions than usual around Northern Australia and Indonesia and can and has been the cause of drought in the past. The third page of the unit looks at climate change as a possible cause of the drought. Australia's climate is changing – but it is not changing in the same way everywhere.

Key ideas

- Global climate patterns mainly result from the circulation of air in the atmosphere, but ocean currents can have a major influence on weather patterns and climate.
- In the Pacific in 'normal' years winds circulate around the Walker cell.
- At certain times the 'normal' situation intensifies and this is known as La Niña.
- During El Niño years pressure systems and weather patterns reverse.
- Apart from the seasons El Niño is the single largest cause of variability in world climate.
- 2002 was the fourth driest year on record in Australia, and also the warmest.
- Australia's climate is changing – but it is not the same everywhere.

Unit outcomes

By the end of this unit most students should be able to:
- understand that global climate patterns mainly result from the circulation of air in the atmosphere, but ocean currents can have a major influence on weather patterns and climate;
- draw two simple annotated diagrams to show atmospheric circulation in 'normal' years and El Niño years;
- describe Australia's rainfall and temperature trends shown in the maps from 1970-2006;
- explain what caused the Big Dry.

Ideas for a starter

1 Ask: Who has heard of El Niño? What can you tell me about it?
2 Show students the maps on page 158 of the Student Book showing temperature and rainfall trends for Australia for 1970-2006. Ask them to describe the trends. Was climate change the cause of the drought?

Ideas for plenaries

1 With books closed ask students to explain these terms to the class: the Walker cell; trade winds; La Niña; El Niño; Southern Oscillation Index. Ask them to add them to their dictionary of key terms for 'Extreme weather'.
2 Ask the class: What was the single most important thing you learned today?

The unit in brief

This 3-page unit looks at how Australia is managing its scarce water resources. The first page concentrates on the National Plan for Water Security which focuses on the Murray-Darling Basin and is designed to ensure that the use of rural water becomes sustainable. Australia has other nationwide programmes for water such as the Australian Government water Fund which focuses on water infrastructure and improved management of Australia's water resource. The rest of the unit looks at how faming needs to change in order to become better suited to Australia's environment, and other ways of securing Australia's water supply.

Key ideas

- Australia's available water resources are declining.
- The National Plan for Water Security focuses on the Murray-Darling Basin and is designed to ensure the use of rural water becomes sustainable.
- The Australian Government Water Fund focuses on water infrastructure and improved management of water resources and is a nationwide programme.
- Australia needs to develop farming systems which are better suited to Australia's environment.
- Australia needs to find other ways of securing the water supply.

Unit outcomes

By the end of this unit most students should be able to:
- explain why Australia's water resources are declining;
- name the six key objectives or areas that the National Plan for Water Security is focussing on, and give examples of the action to be taken;
- give examples of the ways in which Australia's farming is changing;
- suggest other methods Australia could adopt to mange its water supplies.

Ideas for a starter

1 Ask a student to read out the newspaper article on page 159 of the Student Book. Which objectives of the National Plan for Water Security can students identify from the article?

2 Show students the table for the National Plan for Water Security. Tell them it focuses on the Murray-Darling Basin. Ask:
   Why should it focus on the Murray-Darling Basin? (Look again at page 152 if students need to jog their memories.)
   Why is it needed? (It is predicted that the amount of water flowing into the basin will decline further, there is evidence of declining rainfall in south-eastern Australia – see the map on page 158 – and water use is increasing.)
   What will it achieve? (Sustainable use of water.)

Ideas for plenaries

1 'Over to you' activity 1 could be used as a plenary.
2 Use 'What do you think?' on page 160. It is intended to be controversial, but it would appear that farming methods need to change if farming is to be sustainable.
3 Ask students to work together to write a paragraph explaining how Australia is managing its scarce water resources.

The unit in brief

This 4-page unit brought the chapter up-to-date at the time it was written. Heavy rain across the UK throughout the summer of 2007 caused flooding in many places, and this unit focuses on Gloucestershire. The impacts of the flooding ranged from the 'normal' in terms of homes being flooded, people being evacuated from houses and rescued from trapped cars, to the unexpected – the flooding of a water treatment plant and an electricity substation. The second half of the unit examines the causes of the rain – the fact that the Jet Stream was further south than usual bringing depressions instead of settled weather to the UK, and looks at how Cheltenham manages flooding.

Key ideas

- The impacts of the flood included flooded homes, damage to roads, and high river levels as well as the shutting down of a water treatment plant (leaving 350 000 people without water) and the flooding of an electricity substation (leaving 48 000 homes without power).
- In late July 2007 some areas of England and Wales received three times the average monthly rainfall in 24 hours – and that caused the flooding.
- The position of the Jet Stream directly over the UK instead of its normal position (passing to the north of Scotland) brought depressions, storms, and heavy rain to the UK in summer 2007.
- There are a variety of flood defences on the River Chelt.
- Sustainable urban drainage systems use a variety of techniques which allow water to infiltrate into pavements, trenches and so on, or provide temporary water storage.

Unit outcomes

By the end of this unit most students should be able to:
- classify the impacts of the flooding into social, economic and environmental impacts;
- explain how the Jet Stream caused the UK's wet summer in 2007;
- explain why Cheltenham flooded;
- describe the River Chelt flood defences and explain how they help to prevent flooding;
- give examples of different types of sustainable urban drainage systems.

Ideas for a starter

1 Show students photos of the flooded Mythe water treatment plant and people collecting bottled water or water from bowsers. Ask: What links these photos? Where is this? Would you expect to be without water in the UK?

2 Ask: Who knows what the Jet Stream is? What has the Jet stream got to do with flooding? Write response on the board, and keep a record of them.

Ideas for plenaries

1 Revisit students' responses from starter **2** and correct or amend students' ideas.

2 'Over to you' activity **1** could be used as a plenary.

3 Use the 'What do you think?' on page 170 of the Student Book to generate a debate about the protection of our key utilities.

4 Add the key vocabulary to students' dictionary of key terms for 'Extreme weather'.

5 Make 10-15 statements about extreme weather in general, or flooding in particular, some true, some false. Ask students to identify those that are true and those that are false. Where statements are false ask students to correct them.

4　Crowded coasts

Chapter outline

Use this chapter outline and the introductory page of the chapter in the Student Book to give students a mental roadmap for the chapter.

4.1　The coast: not all sand and sea Different coasts and how and why they vary

4.2　The shift to the coast How people are increasingly moving to live at the coast

4.3　Crowded coasts: Bournemouth How coastalisation is occurring along the Hampshire and Dorset coast, focusing on Bournemouth

4.4　Conflict on the coast The special nature of the Dorset coast, and how using it for tourism can create conflict

4.5　Industry on the coast: Southampton Water How one stretch of coast is used for industry, and the environmental impacts this has

4.6　Protest on the coast: Dibden Bay The conflict arising from proposals to build a new container port at Dibden Bay on Southampton Water

4.7　The Holderness coast ... going ... going ... How and why some coasts erode rapidly, and the impacts this has

4.8　Managing erosion on the Holderness coast Different methods of tackling erosion at Holderness, and the effects they have

4.9　Thames estuary at risk How and why the Thames estuary is at risk from rising sea levels and flooding

4.10　Can coasts be managed sustainably? Pressures on salt marshes and how they can be managed sustainably

About the topic

- The coastal zone is one of the world's most densely populated areas.
- The coast has huge environmental value.
- There are competing and conflicting land uses on the coast, and increasing development causes pressure.
- Vulnerable and valuable coasts face a growing physical risk from rapid coastal erosion and coastal flooding.
- A variety of coastal management strategies are used.

About the chapter

- This chapter looks at the growth and development of different coasts: Bournemouth, Florida, Spain, and Australia.
- It investigates the pressures on the Dorset and Hampshire coasts caused by tourism and industry.
- The Holderness coast is used as a case study for coastal erosion and managing erosion.
- The Thames estuary is the focus for an area at risk from rising sea levels and flooding, and managing future growth.

Key vocabulary

There is no set list of words in the specification that students must know. However, examiners will use some or all of the following words in the examinations, and would expect students to know them and use them in their answers.

abrasion

anoxic

boulder clay

brownfield sites

coastal squeeze

coastalisation

container port

corrasion

corrosion

cost-benefit analysis (including tangible and intangible)

downsizing

estuary

eustatic and isostatic change

eutrophication

fetch

footloose

freeze-thaw

geology

green belt

hard and soft engineering

hydraulic action

integrated coastal management

inward migration

longshore drift (including swash and backwash)

natural increase

plant succession

relief

ria

salt marsh

seachange

sediment cells

Shoreline Management Plans

slumping

swell

terminal groyne syndrome

topography

weathering

The glossary at the end of this book contains many of these words and phrases. For students, the key word boxes in the chapter or the glossary at the end of the Student Book will help them with the meanings of all.

The coast: not all sand and sea

The unit in brief

This 2-page unit introduces the topic 'Crowded coasts'. It uses a range of photos to show the variety of coastlines surrounding the UK. It investigates how and why coasts vary, and how they are used.

Key ideas

- The coast's topography is related to its geology. The relief is also affected by its geology.
- Coastal relief can determine how the coast is used.
- Coastal populations are increasing in both developed and developing countries.

Unit outcomes

By the end of this unit most students should be able to:

- understand that geology affects a coast's topography and relief;
- draw spider diagrams to show how coasts vary physically, and the variety of human uses of coasts;
- understand that coastal populations are increasing worldwide.

Ideas for a starter

1 Show students the photos from this unit or other photos which show a variety of types of coast. Ask: Why do they vary so much? What are they used for? Why?

2 Show students a video clip (or clips) from the BBC series *Coast*. Use the clips to explore the varied nature of Britain's coastline.

Ideas for plenaries

1 'Over to you' activity 1 could be used as a plenary.

2 Use the 'What do you think?' on page 175 of the Student Book to get students thinking about whether there are areas of coasts that should be protected and not be developed. This issue will be returned to later in the chapter.

3 Create an acrostic. Write 'CROWDED COASTS' down the side of a page. Use each letter as the first letter of a word, phrase, or sentence about coasts. This may help students to recall information they have learned either in KS3 or during their GCSE course.

4 Give students a photo of a coastal environment. Ask them to annotate it to show physical and human features, opportunities, and possible pressures.

The unit in brief

This 2-page unit explores coastalisation – the movement of people to the coast. Coastalisation is happening in many parts of the world, and Australia, Spain, and Florida are used as examples here. Coastalisation can create a variety of problems and can also mean that people are at risk from erosion and rising sea levels.

Key ideas

- Coastalisation is the movement of people to coastal areas.
- Coastalisation can lead to problems.
- Coastalisation can put people at risk from erosion and rising sea levels.
- In Australia coastalisation is referred to as sea change and there are four main factors causing the sea change.
- The increase in population on Spain's Mediterranean coast and the Florida coast is cause by inward migration.

Unit outcomes

By the end of this unit most students should be able to:
- define coastalisation;
- describe the problems that coastalisation can lead to for one specific location;
- understand that people living in coastal areas are at risk from rising sea levels and erosion;
- draw a spider diagram to classify the factors that have led to coastalisation in Australia, Spain, and Florida.

Ideas for a starter

1. Ask a student to read out Adam's blog on page 177 of the Student Book to introduce the idea of coastalisation.
2. Show students the map showing average population change in Spain on page 177 of the Student Book. Ask them to describe the changes. Ask for suggestions for the increase in population on the Mediterranean coast.
3. Show students photos of a variety of coastal areas from around the world. Who would want to live there? Why?

Ideas for plenaries

1. Use the 'What do you think?' on page 177 of the Student Book to start a discussion on the problems that coastalisation can cause.
2. Start a dictionary of key vocabulary for 'Crowded coasts'. Begin with the terms coastalisation, sea change, inward migration.
3. Make a graffiti wall of what students have learned today.

The unit in brief

Units 4.3–4.6 focus on the issues affecting the stretch of coast between Dorset and Hampshire, and this 4-page unit concentrates on Bournemouth. A Background box explains the growth of UK seaside resorts. Unlike some resorts, which have declined and become run down, Bournemouth is booming. It attracts retired people, but has also retained its younger population. The service sector has seen increasing levels of employment and Bournemouth has attracted footloose industries. Bournemouth's population growth has led to urban expansion causing coastal squeeze – where development has to fit into less space.

Key ideas

- Many coastal counties in the UK are experiencing rapid population growth.
- Bournemouth is growing quickly because of inward migration.
- Most UK seaside resorts date from the Victorian period and have seen similar patterns of growth and decline.
- The service sector has seen increasing levels of employment in Bournemouth – especially in financial institutions.
- The service industries locating in Bournemouth are footloose and are attracted to Bournemouth for specific reasons.
- Population growth has led to urban expansion and subsequent coastal squeeze.

Unit outcomes

By the end of this unit most students should be able to:
- explain Bournemouth's population structure;
- draw a sketch map to show how Bournemouth developed;
- explain why service sector companies have been attracted to locate in Bournemouth;
- describe how Bournemouth's growth has led to coastal squeeze.

Ideas for a starter

1 Ask: Who can remind me what footloose industries are? How do they choose where to locate?
2 Ask students: What do you know about Bournemouth? Where is it? What do you think it is like?
3 Show students the photo on page 179 of the Student Book, or a similar one of Bournemouth. Where do they think this is? What kind of town is it? Is it booming or in decline?

Ideas for plenaries

1 If you used starter **2**, return to students' ideas of what they thought Bournemouth was like. Do their ideas match the reality?
2 Use the 'What do you think?' on page 181 of the Student Book as a plenary. Bournemouth is suffering coastal squeeze. Can it support any further development?
3 Tell your neighbour the two key things you learned today.

Conflict on the coast

The unit in brief

This is a 4-page unit focusing on Dorset's coast. In 2001 UNESCO made the Dorset and East Devon coast a World Heritage Site, placing it alongside places such as Kew Gardens and the Daintree Rainforest in Australia. The first spread in this unit looks at the ecology and geology of the Dorset coast while the second spread looks at the need to protect the coast, tourism, and conflict.

Key ideas

- In 2001 UNESCO made the Dorset and East Devon coast a World Heritage Site – known as the Jurassic Coast.
- Ecologically the Dorset coast is very significant. Much of the area of the Studland sand dunes is an area of SSSI.
- The geology of Dorset's coast is very varied, which has a major impact on landforms.
- World Heritage Status can help to protect the coast – but this can lead to conflict.
- Tourism is Dorset's biggest employer, but tourism brings problems.
- The Boscombe surf reef is intended to bring more surfers, and therefore money to the area and create new jobs.

Unit outcomes

By the end of this unit most students should be able to:
- explain why the ecology of the Dorset coast is significant;
- describe the effect of geology on landforms in Dorset and give named examples of different landforms;
- use a conflict matrix to explain how World Heritage status can lead to conflict;
- describe the problems that tourism can cause;
- identify the advantages and disadvantages of the Boscombe surf reef.

Ideas for a starter

1 Show students the three photos on page 183 of the Student Book. Ask: What is the main factor affecting these landforms (geology)? How does it affect landforms?

2 Who can name some World Heritage Sites? What are they? Where are they? Why are they important? What does World Heritage status mean?

Ideas for plenaries

1 Write the words 'Jurassic Coast' in the middle of your page. Create a mind map around the words. How many ideas can you come up with to do with the Jurassic Coast in 2 minutes?

2 Use the 'What do you think?' on page 185 of the Student Book as a plenary to discuss the advantages and disadvantages of World Heritage Sites.

3 Students can work together to write a paragraph about the problems that tourists cause at Studland Bay.

The unit in brief

This 4-page unit looks at how Southampton Water is used for industry. Southampton Water and the Solent form one of the UK's best natural harbours, but there is competition for land and conflict between different land uses. Fawley oil refinery is used as an example of industry on Southampton Water and the unit investigates the environmental impacts it has. Further impacts that industry has on the coast include sewage and industrial discharge, waste, and metal pollution. The unit includes Background boxes on salt marshes and eutrophication.

Key ideas

- Southampton Water and the Solent form one of the UK's best natural harbours.
- Around Southampton Water there is competition for land and conflict between different land uses.
- Fawley oil refinery is the largest refinery in the UK and has environmental impacts.
- Other industrial impacts on the coast include: sewage and industrial discharge, waste, and metal pollution.
- Salt marshes are important ecologically and economically.
- Eutrophication is the artificial enrichment of water by fertilisers or sewage.

Unit outcomes

By the end of this unit most students should be able to:
- explain why there is competition for land and conflict between different land uses around Southampton Water;
- draw a spider diagram to show the impacts that industry has on the coast;
- explain why salt marshes are valuable;
- identify the strengths, weakness, opportunities, and threats of Southampton Water and the Solent as a location for environmentalists and economic activity.

Ideas for a starter

1. Use the 'What do you think?' on page 188 of the Student Book as a starter to get students thinking about the environmental impacts industry might have on the coast. Record students' ideas.
2. Show students the photo of the dogwhelk on page 189. Ask: What has this got to do with industry? (It is now extinct in Southampton Water because of pollution.)
3. Show students the photo of salt marsh on page 187. What is this? It does not look anything much, why should we protect it?

Ideas for plenaries

1. If you used starter 1 compare students ideas with those covered in this unit. Have students come up with anything not covered here?
2. Use 'Over to you' activity 3 as a plenary.
3. Prepare an odd-one-out for your partner on what you have learned in this unit.

Protest on the coast: Dibden Bay

The unit in brief

This is a 2-page unit which looks at the conflict arising from proposals to build a new container port at Dibden Bay on Southampton Water. In 2001, Associated British Ports (ABP) announced proposals to build a container port at Dibden Bay. ABP felt that Southampton needed the container port in order to make it more competitive. There were many objections to the proposal and in 2004 the Transport Secretary announced that the scheme had not been given planning permission.

Key ideas

- Associated British Ports felt that without the new container port at Dibden Bay Southampton would decline as a port.
- Some people felt that the container port offered economic benefits.
- Other people felt that the environmental damage caused by the container port was not worth it.

Unit outcomes

By the end of this unit most students should be able to:
- explain why ABP wanted to build the new container port;
- assess the main impacts of the container port as economic, social, and environmental, and short, medium, and long term;
- decide whether the decision not to go ahead with the container port was the right one.

Ideas for a starter

1 Show an image of the planned container port at Dibden Bay like the one on page 190 of the Student Book. Ask three students to come to the front of the class and to read the speech bubbles on page 191. Read the Mike Stacey bubble out last. Use this as a way to introduce the issue.

2 Ask: What is a container port? Why would Southampton Water be a good place to build one? (Recap from Unit 4.5 if necessary.)

Ideas for plenaries

1 Use the 'What do you think?' on page 191 of the Student Book to hold a class vote. How many students think jobs and the economy are more important? How many think protecting the environment comes first?

2 Use 'On your own' activity **3** to hold a class discussion. Students can write up the discussion later in 500 words.

3 Take two minutes with a partner to think up one question about Dibden Bay that has not been covered in this unit.

The unit in brief

This unit uses the Holderness coast as a case study of coastal erosion. It is a 6-page unit. Holderness is the fastest eroding coastline in Europe – on average nearly 2 metres of coastline are lost every year. Continued erosion and loss of land has a considerable economic effect on the economy. The unit investigates the three main reasons for rapid erosion at Holderness: geology; fetch; longshore drift and beach material. Background boxes explain the types of processes that are involved in the rapid erosion of the Holderness coast: cliff foot erosion and sub-aerial processes.

Key ideas

- The Holderness coast is the fastest eroding coastline in Europe.
- Coastal erosion has economic impacts.
- The main reasons for rapid erosion of the Holderness coast are geology, fetch, longshore drift and beach material.
- There are two types of processes involved in the rapid erosion of the cliffs on the Holderness coast.
- Cliff-foot erosion processes are: abrasion/corrasion; hydraulic action; corrosion.
- Cliff-face processes are sub-aerial (weathering and mass movement).

Unit outcomes

By the end of this unit most students should be able to:
- understand why erosion of the Holderness coast is so rapid;
- identify the economic, social, and environmental impacts of coastal erosion;
- annotate a map to show how geology, fetch, and longshore drift affect erosion of the Holderness coast;
- define the terms cliff-foot erosion and cliff-face processes;
- draw flow charts to show the step-by-step processes of cliff-foot erosion, weathering on the cliff face, and cliff slumping.

Ideas for a starter

1 Show the photo on page 192 of the Student Book (or a similar image) on the whiteboard. Read Peter Johnson's story aloud to the class.
2 Where is Holdernesss? Who can locate it on a blank map of the UK? What do you know about this stretch of the coast?

Ideas for plenaries

1 Use the 'What do you think?' on page 197 of the Student Book as a plenary. Look again at Peter Johnson's story on page 192. Should Peter Johnson get compensation for the loss of his home, or is it just bad luck?·
2 With books closed ask students to define the key vocabulary from this unit. Then get them to add the words to their dictionary of key terms to do with 'Crowded coasts'.

The unit in brief

In this 6-page unit students investigate different methods of tackling coastal erosion at Holderness, and the effects that they have. Coastal erosion can be prevented – but preventing erosion in one place almost always has impacts somewhere else. A mixture of hard and soft engineering techniques is used along the Holderness coast. These have tended to focus on one particular place. There is now a move to adopt integrated coastal management strategies and devise plans that apply to a whole stretch of coast. Such schemes are called shoreline management plans.

Key ideas

- Hard engineering involves structures built along the coast, usually at the base of a cliff, or on a beach, e.g. sea walls, groynes, and revetements.
- Soft engineering is designed to work with natural processes in the coastal system to try to manage, not necessarily prevent, erosion.
- Managing erosion in one place affects other places, e.g. terminal groyne syndrome.
- A cost-benefit analysis will be carried out before coastal management projects can go-ahead. Costs and benefits are tangible and intangible.
- There is a move to manage sections of the coast as a whole and adopt integrated coastal management strategies.
- Shoreline management plans consider four options: do nothing; hold the line; advance the line; retreat the line.

Unit outcomes

By the end of this unit most students should be able to:
- define hard and soft engineering;
- identify the advantages and disadvantages of the different types of hard and soft engineering used on the Holderness coast;
- explain why and how managing erosion in one place can affect other places;
- understand why integrated coastal management strategies are being adopted;
- describe the options which shoreline management plans consider.

Ideas for a starter

1 Ask: Who can remind me what hard and soft engineering techniques are? Where can they be used?
2 Recap: Why is the Holderness coast being eroded?
3 Show students examples of photos showing hard and soft engineering methods. Use some of the ones in this unit, or any others you have available. Can they identify them? What advantages and disadvantages do they have?

Ideas for plenaries

1 Use 'Over to you' activity 1. If you used starter 3 students can build on their responses.
2 Use the 'What do you think?' on page 202 of the Student Book as a plenary.
3 With books closed ask students to define the key vocabulary from this unit. Then ask them to add it to their dictionary of key terms for this chapter.

The unit in brief

Scientists are predicting that sea level is likely to rise by one metre by 2100 and coastal flooding is likely to increase as a result. Coastal flooding is a serious threat to the UK and this 4-page unit uses the Thames Gateway as a case study to explore the flood risk. It includes a Background box to explain the difference between eustatic and isostatic changes in sea level.

Key ideas

- Coastal flooding is a serious threat to the UK.
- Sea levels can change as a result of eustatic change and isostatic change.
- Sea level change as a result of global warming is an example of eustatic change.
- Rising sea levels and storm surges threaten the Thames Gateway.
- Major new developments are planned for the Thames Gateway.
- The Environment Agency is planning new flood defences to be built along the Thames estuary between 2007 and 2016 to deal with the increased flood risk.

Unit outcomes

By the end of this unit most students should be able to:
- assess the potential flood risk on a selected area of coast;
- explain the difference between eustatic and isostatic changes in sea level;
- understand why the Thames Gateway is at risk from coastal flooding;
- identify the benefits and problems of developing the Thames Gateway;
- describe how the Environment Agency plans to deal with the increased flood risk along the Thames estuary.

Ideas for a starter

1 Show students the photo of the Thames Barrier on page 204 of the Student Book. Ask: What would happen if it failed? What would the impacts be?
2 Brainstorm to find out what students know about the Thames Gateway.

Ideas for plenaries

1 Use the 'What do you think?' on page 207 of the Student Book as a plenary. In the UK (and elsewhere) we continue to build houses in areas at risk from flooding. Why?
2 Use 'Over to you' activity **3** as a plenary.
3 Tell the class the single most important thing you learned today.

The unit in brief

This 2-page unit ends the chapter by looking at the pressure on salt marshes and whether they can be managed sustainably. Coastal estuaries and salt marshes are under pressure from ports, industries such as oil refining, and building. Two-thirds of the Thames estuary salt marsh has been lost since 1945 and the remainder is under pressure. However, efforts are being made to protect the salt marshes and in the case of Abbot's Hall Farm extend them.

Key ideas

- Coastal salt marshes are under pressure from ports, industry, and building.
- The main threats to the Thames estuary salt marsh are building and industry (including the planned new developments for the Thames Gateway), grazing, landfill, fertilisers, drainage, and tourism.
- At Abbot's Hall Farm in Essex the sea has been allowed to breach the sea wall to convert farmland back into salt marsh.
- Different groups have different views on how the coast should be managed.

Unit outcomes

By the end of this unit most students should be able to:
- explain why salt marshes are under pressure;
- explain the issues that the Thames estuary faces;
- assess the benefits and problems caused by converting farmland back into salt marsh at Abbot's Hall Farm;
- explain why different groups are interested in how the Thames estuary is managed.

Ideas for a starter

1 Recap: Show students the photo of salt marsh on page 187 of the Student Book. Say: It does not look much, but who can remind me why it is important, and why we should protect it?
2 Show students the map on page 208 of the Student Book, but minus the key. Who can put a name to the numbers? What are these places used for?

Ideas for plenaries

1 Use the 'What do you think?' on page 209 of the Student Book as a plenary to promote discussion of the value of farmland versus salt marsh.
2 Make up 10–15 statements based on what students have learned about coastal management, some true, some false. Students have to identify the false ones and correct them.
3 Summarise what you have learned today in 35 words.

5 Unequal spaces

Chapter outline

Use this chapter outline and the introductory page of the chapter in the Student Book to give students a mental roadmap for the chapter.

5.1 An unequal nation Spatial, environmental, and socio-economic inequality across the UK

5.2 East Anglia: emerging inequalities The changing characteristics of East Anglia and how places are becoming more unequal

5.3 Managing inequalities in rural East Anglia How inequalities are being managed in North Norfolk and Jaywick, and the problems faced in Southwold and Walberswick

5.4 Can rural communities be sustainable? Some of the things that can be done to create sustainable communities; Cloke's index of rurality

5.5 Planning for the future The plan to build SnOasis to reduce inequalities – but not everyone is in favour

5.6 Botswana: a different kind of inequality Inequalities in a middle income country

5.7 The marginalised Batswana Marginalised groups in rural and urban Botswana, and what is being done to reduce inequalities

5.8 Divided Botswana Two of the contemporary issues that divide Botswana – HIV/AIDS and the move towards sustainable tourism

5.9 Capital inequalities: London Looking at some of the inequalities across London and some of the reasons for them

5.10 A tale of two boroughs Inequalities between Hackney and Hampstead

5.11 Sustainable urban communities Leicester, the Upton Project, and Pathfinder Projects – is sustainable urban living achievable?

About the topic

- 'Unequal spaces' looks at rural and urban inequalities.
- Movements of people, money, and changing opportunities affect both rural and urban areas.
- Some areas struggle and inequalities develop at a variety of scales.
- This topic explores the social, political, and economic causes of disparities.
- It looks at a range of strategies which have been designed to remove or manage inequalities in both rural and urban areas.

About the chapter

- This chapter looks at inequalities in East Anglia, attempts to manage those inequalities, and whether rural communities in the region can be sustainable.
- It investigates rural and urban inequalities in Botswana as well as the issues of HIV/AIDS and the move towards sustainable tourism.
- It also looks at inequalities across London and finally considers sustainable urban living in the UK.

Key vocabulary

There is no set list of words in the specification that students must know. However, examiners will use some or all of the following words in the examinations, and would expect students to know them and use them in their answers.

affordable homes	ripple effect
counter-urbanisation	rural housing enablers
deprivation	rurality
dumb-bell market	rural-urban continuum
environmental magnetism	settlement hierarchy
exception policy	social exclusion
minority group	social landlords
negative externalities	subsistence farming
pandemic	sustainability
positive and negative multipliers	urbanisation and hyper-urbanisation
positive externalities	

The glossary at the end of this book contains many of these words and phrases. For students, the key word boxes in the chapter or the glossary at the end of the Student Book will help them with the meanings of all.

The unit in brief

This 2-page unit begins by looking at the UK's north-south divide to introduce the idea of inequality. The unit then looks at spatial inequality, environmental inequality, and socio-economic inequality. Spatial inequalities exist where the distribution of wealth, resources, and opportunities are not evenly spread, e.g. between urban and rural areas. The section on environmental inequality looks at differences in tranquillity levels across England. In terms of socio-economic inequalities the 2001 Census showed widening inequalities across the UK.

Key ideas

- The UK has a north-south divide and the southern half is dominated by London.
- Spatial inequalities exist where the distribution of wealth, resources, and opportunities are not evenly spread.
- In the countryside, increasing numbers of urban migrants and second home owners create local inequalities in terms of housing.
- The decline of the UK's traditional industries has created socio-economic inequalities.

Unit outcomes

By the end of this unit most students should be able to:

- define spatial inequality, environmental inequality, socio-economic inequality;
- understand why London dominates the southern half of the UK;
- give examples of the obstacles and opportunities faced by people living in urban and rural areas, and explain how they can lead to inequalities;
- draw a diagram to show positive and negative externalities in the local area.

Ideas for a starter

1   Brainstorm: What does inequality mean to you? Do students live in different areas? Do they all have the same access to, for example, public transport and health services?
2   Show students either the two photos on page 208 of the Student Book or similar photos of rural and urban environments. Ask students to think about the advantages (opportunities) and disadvantages (obstacles) of living in these two different places. How can they lead to inequalities?

Ideas for plenaries

1   Start students off building a dictionary of key terms for this chapter. Begin with the key vocabulary in this unit.
2   Use the 'What do you think?' on page 208 of the Student Book as a plenary.
3   If you did not use starter **2** you could do so as a plenary, or use 'Over to you' **1**.

East Anglia: emerging inequalities

The unit in brief

This 4-page unit is the first of a number of case studies of East Anglia. This unit looks at how East Anglia is changing and how the area is becoming more unequal. East Anglia boasts some of the UK's richest landowners and business people, but also has some of the UK's cheapest streets. There are distinctive patterns across the region, but the general picture is one of a region in crisis with a shortage of affordable housing, a decline in services, limited job opportunities, and low levels of child care and health provision.

Key ideas

- East Anglia is an example of the rural-urban continuum.
- There are distinctive patterns across East Anglia.
- Counter-urbanisation has increased throughout East Anglia.
- Communities are changing and rural services are declining.
- The movement of people out of cities has a ripple effect on house prices.
- Increasing house prices and a lack of affordable housing force young people out of the housing market.

Unit outcomes

By the end of this unit most students should be able to:
- define rural-urban continuum, counter-urbanisation, ripple effect, affordable homes;
- identify evidence that proves that East Anglia has its own north-south divide;
- draw a flow diagram to show how counter-urbanisation leads to rural deprivation;
- use evidence to explain why rural services are declining;
- explain why young people are forced out of the housing market.

Ideas for a starter

1 Show students a blank map of East Anglia with just the counties marked on it. Who can identify the counties? What do students know about East Anglia? What images do they have of the region? What inequalities might exist there?
2 Show students two photos – one of Bernard Matthews, one of Jaywick, e.g. the photo on page 210 of the Student Book. Ask: What do these have in common. The answer is you can find them both in East Anglia – but there the similarity ends. They represent the inequalities that exist within the county.

Ideas for plenaries

1 Use the 'What do you think?' on page 213 of the Student Book as a plenary.
2 Write down as many words as you can relating to the work in this unit.
3 You could use 'Over to you' activity **4** or 'On your own' **9** as plenaries.
4 Write this sentence on the board 'The social glue that holds rural communities together is falling apart.' Ask students to unpick it. What does it really mean?

The unit in brief

This is the second unit focusing on East Anglia. It is a 4-page unit which investigates spatial inequalities in three different areas: an Area of Outstanding Natural Beauty (North Norfolk, the most remote and rural part of East Anglia); a declining traditional holiday resort (Jaywick in Tendring, the most deprived area in Essex); and an area with increasing numbers of second homes (Southwold and Walberswick in Waveney).

Key ideas

- Rural communities in East Anglia are in crisis, particularly with regard to housing.
- In North Norfolk AONB more affordable homes have been provided, but this has created a new problem – the dumb-bell market.
- Deprivation and social exclusion in Jaywick has been tackled with the Jaywick Regeneration Masterplan.
- The increasing number of second homes in Southwold and Walberswick has created a social divide and threatens the sustainability of the community.

Unit outcomes

By the end of this unit most students should be able to:
- explain the reasons for the rural housing crisis in East Anglia;
- explain why more affordable housing was needed in North Norfolk, and how it has been provided;
- define or explain the terms rural housing enabler, social landlords, dumb-bell market;
- draw a spider diagram to show the problems that Jaywick had;
- draw a second spider diagram to show how Jaywick tackled its problems;
- identify the economic and social gains and losses of Southwold and Walberswick becoming popular second home locations.

Ideas for a starter

1 Show students the photo of Southwold on page 217 of the Student Book. Read aloud the text box on page 217 which begins 'There is a smell of money…' How many problems can students identify in the text?

2 Ask students: What do these terms mean – 'negative multiplier', 'positive multiplier'? Put the labels from the diagrams on page 214 on the board and ask students to use them to create negative and positive multiplier diagrams.

Ideas for plenaries

1 Use the 'What do you think?' on page 217 of the Student Book to encourage students to think more deeply about the issues that places face.

2 Southwold and Walberswick face serious problems. Ask: What can be done to ensure the sustainability of these communities?

3 Think back over this unit and write down three questions related to what you have learned. The teacher will ask a member of the class to try to answer.

The unit in brief

This 6-page unit explores some of the ways in which communities can change in order to become sustainable. It begins by investigating the criteria for assessing sustainability in East Anglia and goes on to look at a variety of ways of creating sustainable communities ranging from providing homes, services and jobs, to tackling social exclusion and protecting the landscape. The unit includes a Background box which explains rurality and Cloke's index of rurality. It asks whether anywhere in East Anglia will be classified as 'extreme rural' by 2020.

Key ideas

- Sustainability is about meeting the needs of the present generation without compromising the ability of future generations to fulfil their own needs.
- There are a number of ways of creating sustainable communities:
    - Providing homes (central government plans and local schemes)
    - Providing services (community transport, Key Service Centres, combined services)
    - Providing jobs (agricultural and tourism)
    - Tackling social exclusion
    - Protecting the landscape
- As more people who do not depend on the countryside for their livelihood move into a rural area, so the area becomes less rural (its rurality declines).

Unit outcomes

By the end of this unit most students should be able to:
- define the term 'sustainability' and understand the criteria used for assessing sustainability in East Anglia;
- identify the things needed by the rural population, and those which are not being met for different groups;
- draw up a table to show the advantages and disadvantages of the strategies being used to create sustainable communities in East Anglia;
- use the sustainability criteria to assess the strengths and weaknesses of these strategies;
- define the term 'rurality'.

Ideas for a starter

1 Ask: Who can remind me of the definition for the term 'sustainability'?
2 Brainstorm: What ideas can you come up with for creating sustainable communities? Record students' responses.
3 Who can remind me what inequalities and issues rural East Anglia faces?

Ideas for plenaries

1 If you used starter **2** return to the record of student responses. Do these need adding to/amending as a result of what students have learned in this unit?
2 'On your own' activity **8** could be used as a plenary.
3 Give students a blank map of East Anglia. Ask them to annotate it with the ideas included in this unit for creating sustainable communities.

The unit in brief

This unit focuses on the proposal to build Europe's largest indoor winter sports facility – SnOasis – at Great Blakenham in East Anglia. It was seen as one way of reducing rural inequalities. Outline planning permission was granted in 2006, but local opposition to the scheme forced the authorities to hold a public inquiry before work could begin. In addition to providing jobs the scheme planned to double the size of the village, provide affordable homes, build a new railway station, and improve the road network. However, whilst some people believed that the scheme tackled several local social and economic issues, others were against it.

Key ideas

- The site of the SnOasis development is an old Blue Circle cement works and quarry – a brownfield site.
- Great Blakenham has attracted commuters from Ipswich, but lost hundreds of jobs when the cement works and quarry closed in 1999.
- The SnOasis scheme would provide 2000 permanent jobs, new shops and services, 500 new homes (35% affordable), a new railway station, and road improvements.
- The scheme anticipated bringing £50 million a year into the region.
- Some people believed the scheme had major benefits, others thought it was the wrong development in the wrong place.

Unit outcomes

By the end of this unit most students should be able to:
- identify Great Blakenham's needs;
- produce a table to show the benefits and disadvantages that SnOasis would bring to a) Great Blakenham and b) to the region;
- decide whether the SnOasis development is sustainable economically, socially, environmentally;
- recognise that new developments can cause conflict.

Ideas for a starter

1 Show students a range of photos of what SnOasis might look like. You can access a gallery of photos from www.bbc.co.uk/suffolk/dont_miss/snoasis/snoasis.shtml
Ask students what benefits might the development bring to Great Blakenham and East Anglia. Are there any disadvantages?

2 Show the photo on page 224 of the Student Book. Ask individual students to read out the comments of those in favour and those against the SnOasis proposal on page 225. Are jobs and the economy more important than the environment?

Ideas for plenaries

1 You could use this plenary in place of 'Over to you' activity 2. Building on starter 1 ask students to complete the following table and then feedback their results to the rest of the class.

	Advantages	Disadvantages
Economic		
Social		
Environmental		

2 Use the 'What do you think?' on page 225 of the Student Book as a plenary.

Botswana: a different kind of inequality

The unit in brief

This 2-page unit investigates inequalities in Botswana – a middle income country. Botswana grew economically from one of the 10 poorest countries in 1966 to a middle income country by 2006. Its wealth has come from diamond exports, but the wealth is not evenly distributed and huge income disparities exist. Urbanisation has been rapid since 1970, but many people still retain their rural lifestyles.

Key ideas

- Botswana has experienced high rates of economic growth since 1966.
- There are wide income disparities.
- Rapid urban growth and urbanisation is putting strains on infrastructure, service provision, and resources.
- Despite urbanisation many people retain their rural lifestyles.
- The main towns in Botswana attract hundreds of workers who live in villages in their urban shadow.

Unit outcomes

By the end of this unit most students should be able to:
- describe how, and why, Botswana's economy has grown;
- describe and explain income disparities in Botswana;
- use data to show where and why urbanisation happened;
- define the terms urbanisation, primate city, hyper-urbanisation, urban shadow.

Ideas for a starter

1 Show students the photo from page 226 of the Student Book. Use the information in this unit to give students clues about Botswana without mentioning the country's name. Ask students to guess which country you are talking about.

2 Who can remind me what urbanisation and hyper-urbanisation mean? What is a primate city? What is an urban shadow?

Ideas for plenaries

1 Use 'On your own' activity **5** as a plenary. Ask students to suggest ways of reducing poverty in Botswana.

2 Write the phrase 'Inequality in Botswana' in the middle of your page. Create a mind map around the phrase. How many ideas can you come up with in 2 minutes?

3 Get students to add the key vocabulary from this unit to their dictionary of key terms for 'Unequal spaces'.

4 Use the 'What do you think?' on page 227 of the Student Book as a plenary.

The unit in brief

This is a 6-page unit which explores marginalised groups in Botswana and what is being done to reduce inequalities. 48% of Botswana's rural population is poor. Botswana's National Development Plans target rural areas to try and stem the flow of people to the towns. The Remote Area Development Programme aims to help the poorest Batswana, but attempts to move the San Bushmen under the programme were controversial. The last spread looks at the plight of Gabarone's urban poor. Rapid urbanisation has put a strain on services and infrastructure. Many migrants end up in places like Old Naledi. The unit explains how Old Naledi has been upgraded under a Self Help Housing Association Scheme.

Key ideas

- Urban and rural populations in Botswana have the same needs, but there are inequalities in the distribution of land, food, and services.
- Botswana's National Development Plans target rural areas to try to stop people migrating to the towns.
- Remote Area Development Programmes aim to reduce poverty by developing projects in health, education, training, and skills.
- The San Bushmen were moved to new settlements as part of the Remote Area Development Programme.
- Gabarone's rapid urbanisation has put a strain on the provision of services and infrastructure.
- The Self Help Housing Association was set up to provide cheap homes and upgrade Old Naledi.

Unit outcomes

By the end of this unit most students should be able to:
- draw up a table to compare the conditions rural people endure with those endured by urban dwellers;
- draw up a table to show how land rights lead to inequalities;
- explain why the National Development Plans have targeted rural areas;
- explain whether the rural initiatives made the lives of the Remote Area Dwellers better or worse;
- assess the success of the Self Help Housing Association Scheme in Gabarone.

Ideas for a starter

1 Show students the two photos on page 232 of the Student Book. Both are in Gabarone, Botswana. Are students surprised? If so, why? Challenge their views.
2 Recap: Where is Botswana? What type of country is it (i.e. middle income)? Where has its wealth come from? What is the population distribution like?

Ideas for plenaries

1 Use the 'What do you think?' on page 233 of the Student Book as a plenary.
2 Define these terms: marginalised groups, subsistence farming, remote area dwellers, co-operatives, micro-enterprises, Self Help Housing Association. Now get students to add them to their dictionary of key terms for 'Unequal spaces'.
3 Make a graffiti wall of what students have learned in this unit.

The unit in brief

This 2-page unit investigates two of the contemporary issues that divide Botswana – HIV/AIDS and the move towards sustainable tourism. Botswana suffers from the highest rate of HIV/AIDS prevalence in the world and life expectancy rates have fallen dramatically. The government sees tourism as a way of reducing poverty, and income from tourism has increased by 26% in recent years. Botswana's National Ecotourism Strategy has been designed to spread the benefits of tourism in a sustainable way. Although tourism brings in additional income it is not all good news – it can create inequalities by changing local customs and values.

Key ideas

- Botswana suffers from the highest rate of HIV/AIDS prevalence in the world.
- Life expectancy rates have fallen from over 60 years to 35.
- Income from tourism has increased by 26% in recent years and tourism is seen as a way of reducing poverty.
- Botswana's National Ecotourism Strategy has been designed to spread the benefits of tourism in a sustainable way.
- Tourism can create local inequalities by changing local customs and values.

Unit outcomes

By the end of this unit most students should be able to:
- classify the impacts of HIV/AIDS as economic and social, short, medium, and long term;
- explain the significance of HIV/AIDS in terms of Botswana's economic prospects;
- explain why tourism is important in Botswana;
- assess the benefits and problems of tourism in Botswana;
- assess whether tourism can be a sustainable rural initiative if it increases rural inequalities.

Ideas for a starter

1 Show students Botswana's population pyramid on page 234 of the Student Book. The change in the projected population structure for 2020 is dramatic. Ask students what they think is the cause of this. What effect will this have on individuals, families, the population as a whole and the country?
2 Show students the fact box of Botswana's HIV/AIDS statistics. Ask: Why does Botswana have such a high rate of HIV/AIDS? What problems does this create for children?

Ideas for plenaries

1 Use either the 'What do you think?' on page 235 of the Student Book, or 'Over to you' activity **6** as a plenary.
2 What is HIV prevalence? What is a pandemic? What is sustainable tourism?
3 What was the single most important insight you had today? Tell your neighbour.

Capital inequalities: London

The unit in brief

This is a 2-page unit which looks at some of the inequalities across London and the reasons for them. The Index of Multiple Deprivation shows that there is some serious poverty in London. Boroughs with the worst deprivation are all inner city locations. Minority groups are concentrated in specific areas and suffer high levels of unemployment and child poverty. The unit also looks at urban land use and change, and why ethnic enclaves form.

Key ideas

- The Index of Multiple Deprivation (IMD) ranks wards from worst (rank 1), to best (rank 8414).
- London boroughs with the worst deprivation are all inner city locations.
- Minority groups are concentrated in specific areas and have high levels of unemployment and child poverty.
- Different urban zones have different socio-economic characteristics.
- The area around the CBD is a transitional zone where land-use changes.
- Ethnic enclaves form because of proximity to employment opportunities, availability of cheap housing, and the need to stay together.

Unit outcomes

By the end of this unit most students should be able to:
- explain what the IMD shows;
- describe the distribution of deprivation in London;
- explain how social segregation occurs;
- explain why transition zones and ethnic enclaves develop around the CBD.

Ideas for a starter

1   Read out the quote from the Mayor of London on page 236 of the Student Book. Ask students for examples of inequalities in income, employment, and quality of life in the city. You could also do this for any other city that students might be more familiar with.
2   Show students the two photos on page 236. What evidence do they show of inequality?

Ideas for plenaries

1   Provide students with copies of the two photos on page 236 of the Student Book. Stick them on an A3 sheet of paper and use them to create a mind map of inequality in London.
2   With books closed ask different students to define: social segregation, transition zone, social exclusion, ethnic enclave. Now get them to add them to their dictionary of key terms for this chapter.
3   Prepare an odd-one-out for your partner on what you have learned today.
4   Use the 'What do you think?' on page 236 as a plenary.

The unit in brief

This is a 4-page unit which looks at the inequalities between Hackney and Hampstead in London. The unit begins by looking at the differences between Hackney and Hampstead, and at how the government has tried to tackle the problems associated with urban decay since the Second World War. It then goes on to focus on the Nightingale Estate in Hackney, the New Deal initiative in Shoreditch, and Hampstead Garden Suburb – for which the original plans contained most of the ideas now included in twenty-first century regeneration and community projects.

Key ideas

- Huge inequalities exist between Hackney and Hampstead.
- The government has tried a range of strategies to alleviate the problems associated with urban decay.
- Tower blocks replaced terraced housing on the Nightingale Estate in the 1960s and 1970s. In the 1990s the estate was rebuilt.
- A deprivation audit looks at environmental, social, and economic factors.
- The New Deal initiative is about solving long-standing problems by finding bottom-up solutions.
- There are benefits and disadvantages to gentrification.
- The original plans for Hampstead Garden Suburb contained most of the ideas included in twenty-first century regeneration and community projects.

Unit outcomes

By the end of this unit most students should be able to:
- use the data for Hackney and Hampstead to show how quality of life varies;
- construct a table to show how well the Nightingale Estate, Shoreditch, and Hampstead Garden Suburb have dealt with urban problems;
- list the factors that a deprivation audit looks at;
- describe the issues targeted by the New Deal initiative;
- identify four advantages and four disadvantages of gentrification.

Ideas for a starter

1 Show students the table on page 238 of the Student Book. What do these figures show? What do students think these places are like? What do students think it's like to live in Hackney or Hampstead?
2 Ask students what they know about urban regeneration. What strategies are used to regenerate cities? How many ideas can they come up with? Compare their ideas with the list of government strategies on page 238.

Ideas for plenaries

1 Ask students to read out local people's views about the New Deal on page 240 of the Student Book. Use these to generate a discussion on the success of the New Deal in Shoreditch.
2 Is it surprising that the original plans for Hampstead Garden Suburb contained many of the ideas included in current regeneration and community projects?
3 Ask students to work together to write a paragraph on inequalities between Hackney and Hampstead.

The unit in brief

Inner city areas in the nineteenth century had some of the characteristics that today's planners look for when creating sustainable communities. This final 2-page unit considers how cities have changed and the attempts made to create new sustainable communities. It uses the example of Leicester, where the inner city regeneration programme is aiming to bring residential populations back into central Leicester, and smaller scale examples – the Upton Project and Pathfinder Projects.

Key ideas

- Some of the features of typical of inner city areas in the nineteenth century are the characteristics that today's planners use to create sustainable communities.
- Leicester's inner city regeneration programme aims to be sustainable.
- The Upton Project is being developed as a sustainable extension to Northampton.
- Pathfinder Projects aim to upgrade housing quality for home owners in cities suffering from economic decline.

Unit outcomes

By the end of this unit most students should be able to:
- list the characteristics of a sustainable urban community;
- describe how Leicester's regeneration programme aims to make its designated zones sustainable;
- examine the proposals for Leicester, Upton, and Rochdale and complete a SWOT analysis for people, the economy, and the environment.

Ideas for a starter

1 Brainstorm: What makes a community sustainable? You are looking for ideas such as close to places of work, shops, and services; affordable homes; closely-knit communities etc. Record students' responses.
2 Show students the photo of inner city Leicester on page 242 of the Student Book. What characteristics did it have in the nineteenth century that made it sustainable? What problems does it have now?

Ideas for plenaries

1 If you used starter 1 return to the record of students' responses. Do students need to add/amend anything in the light of the work in this unit?
2 Use the 'What do you think?' on page 243 of the Student Book as a plenary.
3 Create an acrostic. Write SUSTAINABLE URBAN COMMUNITIES down one side of the page. Make each letter the first letter of a word, phrase, or sentence about sustainable urban living.

6 Rebranding places

Use this chapter outline and the introductory page of the chapter in the Student Book to give students a mental roadmap for the chapter.

6.1 Rebranding places What 'rebranding places' is all about

6.2 Regeneration in East London The need for regeneration and rebranding in East London

6.3 London and the 2012 Olympics Looking at the impact that a major sports event can have on regeneration

6.4 Transport regeneration in East London The importance of transport in regeneration

6.5 Sydney's Olympic story How successful sports-led regeneration was in Sydney, and what we mean by sustainability

6.6 Re-imaging Manchester How music and leisure can be used to regenerate and re-image cities

6.7 Can Walton-on-the-Naze be resuscitated? How rebranding is needed in the traditional British seaside resort

6.8 Cornwall in crisis? Deprivation in a rural area

6.9 Cornwall's Garden of Eden? How flagship projects for re-imaging rural areas can bring major benefits

6.10 Rebranding 'cool' Cornwall How investment in rural areas can help regeneration

6.11 Rebranding farming How farmers can survive by rebranding their farm businesses

6.12 Can rebranding apply to LEDCs? How rebranding rural areas in LEDCs is just as essential as in MEDCs, and can have major impacts

About the topic

- Rebranding is about both re-imaging and regeneration.
- Rebranding is needed in both urban and rural areas.
- There is a wide range of strategies that places use to reinvent themselves.
- This topic explores why rebranding is necessary and considers how public and/or private funding can be used to implement flagship and community projects to improve the social fabric, lifestyle, environment, and economy of places.

About the chapter

- This chapter investigates what rebranding is and why it is needed in some places; who the rebranding players are, and what strategies exist for places to rebrand themselves; urban and rural rebranding.
- It includes a number of detailed case studies: regeneration in East London; London and the 2012 Olympics and Sydney's Olympics; re-imaging Manchester; rebranding in Walton-on-the-Naze; investment and regeneration in Cornwall including the Eden Project; and rebranding in Uganda.

Key vocabulary

There is no set list of words in the specification that students must know. However, examiners will use some or all of the following words in the examinations, and would expect students to know them and use them in their answers.

affluent
affordable housing
brownfield sites
container port
core and periphery
cost-benefit analysis
deprivation
destination tourism
diversify
eco-approaches to farming
economic leakage
fertility rate
footloose industry
greenfield sites
index of deprivation
infrastructure

inward migration
key players
legacy
market-led regeneration
multiplier effect
multiple index of deprivation
negative multiplier
post-production countryside
poverty trap
primary employment
remittance payments
subsidies
subsistence farming
sustainable development
tangible and intangible costs
transport hub

The glossary at the end of this book contains many of these words and phrases. For students, the key word boxes in the chapter or the glossary at the end of the Student Book will help them with the meanings of all.

The unit in brief

This 2-page unit is an introduction to the whole idea of 'rebranding places' and explains what rebranding is all about. It uses Doncaster as an example of a place that needed rebranding having been hard hit by the decline of its traditional industries. The development of the Robin Hood airport is seen as one way of rebranding the area. A Background box explains that places need to rebrand because of economic change – the decline in primary and secondary industries and the growth of tertiary industries.

Key ideas

- Doncaster (and Rossington) has suffered from the decline in its traditional primary and secondary industries.
- Rebranding is the way, or ways, in which a place is redeveloped and marketed so that it gains a new identity. It can then attract new investors and visitors.
- The development of Doncaster's new airport is one way of rebranding the area.
- Places need to rebrand because of economic change caused by the decline in primary and secondary industries, and the growth of tertiary industries (particularly tourism).

Unit outcomes

By the end of this unit most students should be able to:
- outline why the Doncaster area needed rebranding;
- explain how Doncaster's new airport might help in rebranding the area;
- explain how the decline of primary and secondary industries and subsequent growth of tertiary industries means that places need to rebrand;
- complete a table showing different ways of rebranding industrial sites in a local area.

Ideas for a starter

1 Use examples from the Student Book and show students photos of areas before and after rebranding as a way of introducing the idea, e.g. London Docklands and Canary Wharf on pages 248–249 and Manchester pages 262–263.
2 Ask students if they can think of local examples of rebranding, e.g. a local school or college changing its name or logo etc. Why did it rebrand? Has the rebranding been successful?

Ideas for plenaries

1 Ask students: What does rebranding mean? Why do places need to rebrand? Give me some examples of places that you know about that need rebranding.
2 Get students to start a dictionary of key terms for Rebranding places using the key vocabulary in this unit.
3 Sum up what you have learned today in 40 words or less and tell you neighbour.

The unit in brief

This is a 4-page unit which looks at the need for regeneration and rebranding in East London. It investigates why regeneration was needed in London Docklands and the development of Canary Wharf. The Docklands regeneration has been criticised for failing to make an impact on local people and the environment and the unit compares Canning Town and Millwall (the location of Canary Wharf). Canning Town is not far from Canary Wharf but has low levels of employment and few people play a part in Canary Wharf's growing economy. The results of a survey carried out by Queen Mary College University of London which assessed the needs and quality of life of people living in Canning Town are included on the last page of the unit. The unit also includes Background boxes on how cities were regenerated in the 1980s and how regeneration takes place.

Key ideas

- Economic decline caused by industrial and dock closures in East London in the 1970s and early 80s led to massive unemployment.
- Docklands offered a large area of land for redevelopment. Key features include the Canary Wharf building and other huge skyscrapers.
- Transport developments were completed to help regeneration.
- Other cities suffered deprivation in the 1980s and a variety of schemes have been developed to regenerate cities.
- Regeneration involves a variety of key players.
- Market-led regeneration is where private companies make decisions about development and are given benefits.
- Despite Docklands regeneration East London suffers deprivation, poor health and poor environmental quality.

Unit outcomes

By the end of this unit most students should be able to:
- explain why regeneration was needed in East London and other inner cities;
- describe how Canary Wharf was regenerated;
- understand that regeneration involves a variety of key players;
- draw graphs to show that Canning Town shows evidence of deprivation.

Ideas for a starter

1 Ask: What do you know about London Docklands? Students may have learned about Docklands at GCSE and be aware of some of the regeneration issues.
2 Recap: Who can remind me what rebranding is? Why do places need to rebrand?

Ideas for plenaries

1 'Over to you' activities **1** and **2** could be used as plenaries, as could 'On your own' **10**.
2 Use the 'What do you think?' on page 250 of the Student Book as the basis for a discussion on the benefits and disadvantages of regeneration.
3 Tell your neighbour the three key things you learned today.

The unit in brief

This unit uses the London 2012 Olympics as a 4-page case study to investigate the impact that a major sports event can have on regeneration. London was said to have won the Olympic bid because it plans to use the Games as a way of regenerating East London. The Olympics involve huge expense and costs need to be weighed against benefits. The Olympics involve a number of key players. The decisions made by these organisations have impacts on the local economy, the local environment and on local people.

Key ideas

- London plans to use the 2012 Olympics as a way of regenerating East London.
- The Olympics must leave a legacy of sustainable impacts if they are to be successful.
- The Olympic bid was made on the basis that benefits would exceed costs.
- Decisions made by the key players impact the local economy, people and environment.
- Impact on the local economy – the site of the main Olympic facilities is an industrial estate. All the companies had to move.
- Impact on the local environment – the collapse of manufacturing led to dereliction in the area that will house the Olympic Park. The area will be re-landscaped to create a new London park and improve environmental quality.
- Impact on local people – building the Olympic Village meant demolishing existing housing. After the Olympics the Village will be remodelled into affordable housing.

Unit outcomes

By the end of this unit most students should be able to:
- understand that London plans to use the 2012 Olympics as a way of regenerating East London;
- identify the costs and benefits of staging the London Olympics;
- understand that decisions made by the key players impact the local economy, environment and people;
- say how far the Olympics will leave a legacy of environmental gain;
- summarise the economic and social gains and losses of the Olympics for the local area.

Ideas for a starter

1 Show students the photo on page 252 of the Student Book, or similar photos of people celebrating London's successful Olympic bid. Ask: What benefits might the Olympics bring to London? What costs (tangible or intangible) might be incurred?
2 Brainstorm: What is the link between sport (or the Olympics) and regeneration? Record responses on the whiteboard.

Ideas for plenaries

1 If you used starter **2** go back to the responses you recorded. Can you add anything else?
2 Ask students to work in pairs to write a paragraph on the impact of the Olympics on the local economy, the local environment, or local people.
3 Use the 'What do you think?' on page 255 of the Student Book to discuss the likely success of the 2012 Olympics from an economic, social, and environmental point of view.
4 'Over to you' **1** and **4** could be used as plenaries.

6: Rebranding places

Transport regeneration in East London

The unit in brief

This 2-page unit looks at the importance of transport in regeneration. Stratford in East London had been geographically isolated from the rest of London because of poor east-west transport links across the city. This in turn led to a negative multiplier effect. Transport links have now been improved, by the time of the London Olympics Stratford will be able to handle 500 000 people a day, and Stratford now has many geographical advantages over the rest of London. Further transport improvements mean that Stratford is now seen as an economic growth area of London. The biggest planned project is Stratford City – a major commercial development.

Key ideas

- Stratford had been isolated from the rest of London because of poor east-west transport links across the city.
- Stratford's isolation led to a negative multiplier effect, with low development and investment and high unemployment.
- Transport links had to be improved in order to win the Olympic bid
- Further improvements to transport mean that Stratford has become a transport hub and is a major economic growth area.
- The biggest planned project is Stratford City.

Unit outcomes

By the end of this unit most students should be able to:
- explain why Stratford had been neglected and isolated;
- draw a positive multiplier diagram to show how Stratford and East London might change;
- give examples of the improvements to Stratford's transport links;
- explain why the new CTRL station is so important to East London's' regeneration;
- describe the impacts Stratford City is likely to have.

Ideas for a starter

1 Draw the negative multiplier on page 256 of the Student Book on the whiteboard. What does it show? Do students know anywhere that this diagram could describe? How could it be changed? Ask students to devise a positive multiplier diagram.
2 Ask: Who can tell me how transport developments can help in regeneration? (The development of transport infrastructure can give an economic boost. This was the case in Shanghai and is part of what Vision Mumbai is aiming to do – see Unit 2.11. Although these cities are on a different scale the end result in terms of economic growth may be similar.)

Ideas for plenaries

1 Ask students: What is a negative multiplier, transport hub, and economic leakage? Add them to the dictionary of key terms to do with rebranding places.
2 Use the 'What do you think?' on page 257 of the Student Book as a plenary.
3 Write the phrase 'Regeneration in East London' in the middle of the page. Create a mind map around the phrase. How many ideas can students add in 2 minutes?

The unit in brief

This unit is about sports-led regeneration in Sydney, and sustainability. These 4 pages look at Sydney's plan to hold the world's first 'Green' Olympics in 2000. The plan started with the Olympic Village and was the extended to the design of the whole Olympic Park. The unit includes a photo which shows how contaminated the Olympic site was. A huge amount of cleaning up went on, and though not perfect the site is better than it was. A Background box explains what sustainability is and the rest of the unit considers whether Sydney's Olympics were sustainable economically, socially and environmentally.

Key ideas

- The Olympics offer cities a chance to use investment in sport as an opportunity for regeneration.
- Sydney planned to hold the first 'green' Olympics.
- Homebush Bay, the site of the Olympic Park, was badly contaminated and new ways had to be found to reduce the contamination.
- Sustainability is 'the ability to provide for the needs of the world's current population without damaging the ability of future generations to provide for themselves.'
- Sydney's Olympics can be judged on their economic, social and environmental sustainability.

Unit outcomes

By the end of this unit most students should be able to:
- explain how investment in sport can provide opportunities for regeneration;
- give examples of the criteria use for a 'green' Olympics;
- classify statements on economic sustainability and explain which part of Australia benefited most from the Olympics and whether benefits were short, medium or long term;
- decide whether the social issues were a price worth paying for the Olympics;
- say how well Sydney provided a 'Green' Olympics.

Ideas for a starter

1 Draw a spider diagram on the board. In the central bubble write the word 'sustainability'. In three other bubbles write 'economic sustainability', 'social sustainability' and 'environmental sustainability'. Remind students of the definition of sustainability. Can they work out definitions for economic, social and environmental sustainability? Check what they come up with against the background box on page 259 of the Student Book.
2 Ask students how they could plan a green Olympics. Can they come up with a list of criteria in terms of economic, social and environmental issues? How well does their list of criteria match the criteria on page 258 of the Student Book?

Ideas for plenaries

1 Use 'Over to you' **5** (the debate) as a plenary.
2 Work with a partner. Read the 'What do you think?' on page 260 of the Student Book and write 75 words in response to the question.
3 Make up 10 statements based on what students have learned so far about rebranding and regeneration – some true, some false. Students have to identify and correct the false ones.

The unit in brief

In this 2-page unit students find out how music and leisure has been used to regenerate and re-image Manchester. Manchester's declining economy had left the city with an image problem. The City Council developed a policy of re-imaging the city involving music, television, sport and culture. A good transport infrastructure and the availability of cheap property were also crucial to Manchester's successful re-imaging. The unit also looks at the issues Manchester faces in the future. It may not be easy maintaining Manchester's new image.

Key ideas

- Manchester's economic collapse in the 1980s left it with derelict industrial land, poor housing and an image problem.
- Manchester City Council developed a policy of re-imaging the city involving music, television, sport and culture.
- The city's transport infrastructure and availability of cheap property were crucial to Manchester's successful re-imaging.
- Manchester faces issues for the future:
  - property is no longer cheap
  - clubs face pressure from organised crime
  - magistrates and police cannot manage the sector effectively
  - there are problems in the provision of safe, late-night transport.

Unit outcomes

By the end of this unit most students should be able to:
- explain why Manchester needed re-imaging;
- decide which of a range of factors played the greatest part in re-imaging Manchester;
- decide how serious the four future issues will be for Manchester.

Ideas for a starter

1 Ask students: If sport can be used to rebrand and regenerate places what else could be used? You are looking to elicit music, television, culture etc.
2 Show students a range of photos, e.g. some of the bands that have come out of Manchester such as Oasis, the Happy Mondays etc., stills or scenes from television programmes such as Coronation Street, Shameless, Clocking Off (or others set in Manchester) or Manchester United or Manchester City football clubs. Ask students to think about what these images have in common. They are all connected with Manchester and Manchester City Councils' policy of re-imaging the city using music, television, sport and culture.

Ideas for plenaries

1 Which other cities have used music, sport or culture to develop their image?
2 What else could places use to change their image/rebrand themselves?
3 Use the 'What do you think?' on page 263 of the Student Book to get students thinking about whether music is really a good basis for regenerating cities.
4 Write down three questions related to what you have learned today. The teacher will ask a member of the class to try to answer the questions.

The unit in brief

This unit looks at how rebranding is needed in a traditional British seaside resort, using Walton-on-the-Naze in Essex as a case study. In the 1950s and 60s the town was in its heyday, but now it is declining and has an ageing population. It is in desperate need of rebranding and this 2-page unit investigates the possible options Walton-on-the-Naze could use to rebrand itself.

Key ideas

- Walton-on-the-Naze was in its prime as a traditional British seaside resort in the 1950s and 60s.
- Walton-on-the-Naze has declined as a result on longer holidays, higher incomes, increased car ownership, and cheaper overseas travel.
- Walton-on-the-Naze has an ageing population.
- There are a number of options open to Walton-on-the-Naze for it to rebrand itself.

Unit outcomes

By the end of this unit most students should be able to:
- understand that traditional British seaside resorts were in their prime in the 1950s and 60s;
- explain why resorts such as Walton-on-the-Naze have declined;
- explain why traditional seaside resorts have a cycle of poverty;
- identify the advantages and disadvantages of the options Walton-on-the-Naze has to rebrand itself;
- assess which rebranding options would work best for Walton-on-the-Naze.

Ideas for a starter

1 Ask students to name four traditional British seaside resorts. What image do they conjure up? What would they have been like 50 years ago? You are looking to elicit that some of them, like Walton-on-the-Naze may have been bustling in the 1950s and 60s, but are now in decline.

2 Show students photos of British seaside resorts today – in decline and looking 'tired'. Think about what you learned so far about rebranding. How could these places be rebranded for the twenty-first century?

Ideas for plenaries

1 Use the 'What do you think?' on page 265 of the Student Book as a plenary. Is it possible to rebrand our ageing seaside resorts?

2 'Over to you' activity **2** could be used as a plenary.

3 Describe Walton-on-the-Naze's population structure. How does it compare with the UK average? What problems does this cause the town?

4 Are there any other options for rebranding Walton-on-the-Naze which have not already been mentioned? Use your imaginations!

The unit in brief

This 4-page unit investigates deprivation in a rural area and uses Cornwall as the case study. Cornwall is the UK's top destination for family holidays and short breaks – yet the county is in crisis and in need of regeneration. Cornwall is one of Europe's most deprived areas. The unit looks at how deprivation has been caused by low wages, decline in the rural economy, a lack of rural services and lack of employment opportunities. A Background box on core and periphery theory helps to explain that the main reason for deprivation in rural areas such as Cornwall is their remoteness.

Key ideas

- Cornwall is the UK's top holiday destination for family holidays and short breaks.
- Cornwall suffers deprivation caused by:
  - low wages
  - decline in the rural economy
  - lack of rural services
  - lack of employment opportunity (all leading to a cycle of deprivation).
- Tourism has helped to offset some job losses in primary industries but creates other problems.
- The main reason for deprivation in rural areas is their remoteness. Core and periphery theory explains this.
- Cornwall has the fastest growing population of any UK county due to inward migration.

Unit outcomes

By the end of this unit most students should be able to:
- classify the causes of Cornwall's fall in primary employment;
- construct a cycle of deprivation to explain why villages have few services;
- explain how lack of employment opportunities leads to a cycle of deprivation;
- identify the problems that tourism creates;
- understand core and periphery theory in relation to Cornwall's deprivation.

Ideas for a starter

1 Show students the photo of the Cornish countryside on page 266 of the Student Book, or a similar image. Ask a student to read out the quote from Andrew Mitchell on page 266. Ask: What problems could Cornwall face? Why is it one of Europe's' most deprived areas? Why is it in crisis?

2 Show students the graph of seasonal unemployment on page 267 of the Student Book. What problems does this cause? You are looking for suggestions such as employment is likely to be in tourism which may be part-time and poorly paid; low incomes result in low spending power, limiting business opportunities; people can't afford housing; councils receive lower taxes and cannot invest in infrastructure and local services – all creating a cycle of deprivation.

Ideas for plenaries

1 With books closed ask individual students to explain key terms from the unit to the rest of the class. Then get them to add the terms to their dictionary of key terms for 'Rebranding places'.

2 What was the single most important thing you learned today? Write it down.

3 Use the 'What do you think?' on page 269 of the Student Book as a plenary.

The unit in brief

This unit continues using Cornwall as a case study to find out how flagship projects for re-imaging rural areas, such as the Eden Project, can bring major benefits. The Eden Project opened in 2001 and in its first year attracted 1.9 million visitors. Building the Eden Project in the bottom of a china clay pit helped to re-image the environment. It has brought major benefits to the area and the local economy, but has also caused some problems.

Key ideas

- Building the Eden Project in the bottom of a china clay pit was an opportunity to re-image the environment.
- The Eden Project has created problems in terms of its impact on traffic levels and pollution and air quality.
- The Eden Project has benefited the local economy in terms of: visitor numbers and spending; demand for accommodation; employment; impact on local producers and other attractions.
- The Eden Project has had a multiplier effect on the local economy.

Unit outcomes

By the end of this unit most students should be able to:
- classify the problems and benefits created by the Eden Project as economic, social, environmental;
- explain whether the benefits the Project has brought are worth the problems it has created;
- describe how the Eden Project has had a multiplier effect on the local economy.

Ideas for a starter

1 Use the 'What do you think?' on page 271 of the Student Book to recap Unit 6.8.
2 Show students the photo of the Eden Project on page 270 of the Student Book. Brainstorm to find out what benefits a project like this can bring to a deprived area. Record students' responses.

Ideas for plenaries

1 If you used starter **2** refer back to students responses. Add to, or amend, the benefits that projects like the Eden Project can bring to a deprived area in the light of this unit.
2 Debate the statement 'Economic benefits outweigh environmental impacts' in terms of the Eden Project. Students can then write 400 words summing up the debate in place of 'On your own' activity **6**.
3 Take 2 minutes with a partner to think up one interesting question about how projects like the Eden Project can benefit rural areas that has not been covered in this unit.

The unit in brief

This unit uses 4 pages to continue the Cornwall theme and looks at how investment in rural areas can help regeneration. Cornwall needs to diversify to create an all-year round economy not one that just thrives in the summer. The main attempt to rebrand Cornwall and attract new tourists is destination tourism, and the Eden Project is an example of this. Cornwall gained EU Objective One Funding in 1999 which is designed to boost the local economy. The unit includes a Background box to explain Objective One funding and five examples of projects funded by Objective One.

Key ideas

- Cornwall needs to diversify to create a year-round economy.
- The main concept in rebranding Cornwall to attract new tourists is destination tourism.
- Objective One funding aims to reduce social and economic differences within the EU and boost the local economy.
- Objective One has helped the Cornish economy to grow faster than the UK average.
- Objective One has funded many projects in Cornwall but they do not all succeed.

Unit outcomes

By the end of this unit most students should be able to:
- understand why Cornwall needs to create a year-round economy;
- give two factors that have helped to promote destination tourism;
- assess the success of projects funded by Objective One and reach an agreed order for the best projects;
- explain how well Objective One benefits Cornwall.

Ideas for a starter

1. Ask students what they think destination tourism is. You might need to help them out a bit – tell them that the Eden Project is one example of this.
2. Recap: Why does Cornwall need to rebrand itself?
3. Show students the photo of Watergate Bay on page 272 of the Student book. Has can this asset be used to help Cornwall rebrand itself?

Ideas for plenaries

1. Add the key vocabulary from this unit to your dictionary of key terms for 'Rebranding places'.
2. Ask students how far they agree with Professor Gripaios' claim that as far as Objective One funding was concerned 'the jam has been spread too thinly on too many projects'.
3. Use the 'What do you think?' on page 275 of the Student Book as a plenary. Would it have been better to give the Objective One funding to the poorest 5% of the Cornish population? Would that have benefited the local economy in the same way?

The unit in brief

This 2-page unit investigates the crisis in farming in the UK. Farm incomes fell drastically between 1973 and 2003 and many farmers earn less than the national minimum wage. Farming collapsed due to the strength of the pound and competition between supermarkets which have driven prices down. The unit looks at how some farms are now rebranding what they do in order to increase incomes. Lobb's Farm Shop is used as a case study. The shop was financed using funding from Objective One and central government and has created new jobs as well as providing a visitor centre and improving environmental quality and animal welfare.

Key ideas

● Farm incomes fell sharply between 1973 and 2003.
● The two main reasons for the fall in farm incomes are the strength of the pound and the power of supermarkets.
● Some farms are rebranding what they do in an attempt to increase incomes.
● Lobb's Farm Shop is one example of how a farm has rebranded itself, and created other benefits.

Unit outcomes

By the end of this unit most students should be able to:
● draw a flow chart to explain how the strength of the pound and the power of supermarkets have led to many farmers giving up;
● give examples of the ways in which farms can rebrand what they do;
● classify the benefits Lobb's Farm Shop has brought into economic, social and environmental.

Ideas for a starter

1 Show students the graph of farm incomes on page 276 of the Student Book. Ask them for suggestions for the fall in farm incomes shown on the graph.
2 Show students the first three columns of the table on page 276 of the Student Book. Brainstorm the likely implications when comparing costs of production and farm prices. Do their ideas match the implications given in the table?
3 How can farms rebrand in order to increase incomes and stay in business? Students may have studied farm diversification at GCSE and may already have some ideas. They just may not have thought of them in terms of rebranding.

Ideas for plenaries

1 With books closed ask students to explain key terms from this unit to the rest of the class. Then ask them to add them to their dictionary of key terms for 'Rebranding places'.
2 'On your own' activity **6** could be used as a plenary.
3 Use the 'What do you think?' on page 277 of the Student Book to get students thinking about their values and attitudes towards farming.

Can rebranding apply to LEDCs?

The unit in brief

This final unit in 'Rebranding places' looks at how rebranding rural areas in LEDCs is just as essential as in MEDCs and can have major impacts. Uganda is used as the case study in this 4-page unit which starts with a factfile on the country. It looks at how communities become locked in a poverty trap and then investigates two projects – the Equatorial College School and the Village Phone Initiative – which try to improve people's image of rural areas and the rural poverty trap.

Key ideas

- Much of the farming in Uganda is subsistence farming, rural incomes are low.
- Communities become locked in a poverty trap.
- AIDs has made the poverty trap worse.
- Equatorial College School relies on fees and UK fund-raising and the first exam results were the best in the region.
- The purpose of the Village Phone Initiative is to stimulate rural business and reduce rural isolation.

Unit outcomes

By the end of this unit most students should be able to:
- explain why rural communities in Uganda become locked in a rural poverty trap;
- draw a diagram to show how AIDS has made the poverty trap worse in Uganda;
- draw a table to show how girls secondary education affects Uganda's fertility rate;
- assess how the Equatorial College School and the Village Phone Initiative can help to rebrand Uganda's rural areas.

Ideas for a starter

1 Ask students: Where is Uganda? Can they locate it on a blank map of Africa?
2 Show students the table in the Uganda factfile on page 278 of the Student Book. Use it to discuss how the two countries compare. Start with indicators that are meaningful and relevant to students, e.g. numbers of fixed line and mobile phone subscribers and internet users.

Ideas for plenaries

1 Use the 'What do you think?' on page 281 of the Student Book as a plenary. Will the Village Phone Initiative result in increasing consumerism in rural Africa? What could the impacts of this be?
2 Summarise what you have learned in this unit in less than 40 words.
3 Do a fun alphabet run from A-Z to sum up 'Rebranding places'. Ask students for a word or phrase to do with 'Rebranding places' for each letter of the alphabet.

Exams: how to be successful

Chapter outline

What is the Edexecel AS Geography Specification all about? What it is all about, and what it includes

How will you be assessed? What the exams are like

Know your exam papers What the questions will be like, command words, interpreting the questions

How to use case studies in the exam A portfolio of case studies, how to remember your case study – and using it

How to use fieldwork and research in the exam Understanding the question, focusing the question, answering the question

How are the exam papers marked? Point marking, level marking

How to gain marks and not lose them

About the chapter

- This chapter is intended to help students to be successful.
- They need to know and understand the geography that they have been studying, but they also need to know how they will be examined, what kinds of questions they will come up against in the exam, how to use what they know, and what they will get marks for. That is where this chapter can help.
- Fieldwork and research skills are a key feature of Unit 2 Geographical investigations.
- Whichever two topics students have studied they will be expected to use fieldwork and research in the exam, so this chapter tells them how to do it.

Command words

There is no key vocabulary for this chapter, but students do need to understand what the command words used in the exam questions mean. These are some of the most commonly used command words. Their meanings are given in the Student Book.

account for	evaluate
analyse	examine
assess	explain
comment on	how far?
compare	illustrate
contrast	justify
define	list
describe	outline
discuss	to what extent?

Glossary

*= a cross-reference

A

abrasion – the grinding away of bedrock by fragments of rock which may be incorporated in ice. Also known as corrasion

adaptation – any change in the structure or functioning of an organism or system that makes it better suited to the environment

affluent – having a lot of money and a good standard of living

affordable homes – homes which can be afforded by young adults on or below the average wage. The US guideline is that they should not cost more than 30% of a household's gross income

anoxic – without oxygen

at-risk zones – inhabited areas most at risk from natural disasters

B

baby boom – any period of greatly increased birth rate during a certain period, and usually within certain geographical bounds. Persons born during such a period are often called baby boomers

boreal forest – evergreen forests which occur naturally between 55° and 66° North where winters are long and very cold. Also known as coniferous forest

boulder clay – the unsorted sediment deposited directly below a glacier, which has a range of particle size from fine clay to rock fragments and boulders. Also known as glacial till

burakumin – a Japanese social group associated with 'dirty' occupations and discriminated against by other people

C

carbon credits – a way to reduce greenhouse gas emissions in industry by putting a value and a limit on a company's emissions and allowing the company to sell its emissions shortfall or to buy carbon credits if it exceeds its limit. Carbon credits can be used to finance carbon reduction schemes

carbon offsetting – the act of *mitigating greenhouse gas emissions, e.g. by asking people or companies to pay extra for air travel

carbon sinks – reservoirs of carbon dioxide. The main natural sinks are the oceans and plants that use photosynthesis to remove carbon from the atmosphere

centrally planned economy – a country where (nearly) all business and industry is controlled by the state

chalk – a pure form of limestone consisting of the shells of tiny marine organisms together with egg-shaped particles of calcium carbonate

chemical fertilisers – compounds given to plants to promote growth. Fertilizers can be organic (composed of organic matter), or inorganic (made of simple, inorganic chemicals or minerals)

coastal squeeze – a) where a coastal settlement is prevented from expanding due to the sea on one side and rural areas inland b) an environmental situation where the coastal margin is squeezed between the fixed landward boundary (artificial or otherwise) and the rising sea level

coastalisation – the movement of people to coastal areas. It can be used in the negative sense of intensive housing development along coastlines, leading to environmental degradation

cold front – a *front where the cold air pushes in behind the warm air

congestion charging – making road users pay to drive in a particular city

conservative plate boundary – where the movement of tectonic plates is parallel to the margin. It is also known as a transform fault

container – a metal box of standard size, used for the transport of cargo by road, rail or water

convergence – in meteorology, when airstreams flow to meet each other, leading to an increase in the height of the atmosphere, which often causes weather events; in plate tectonics, when two plates come together

core and periphery – a model of development which tries to represent the emergence of an urban system in four major stages. In between the affluent core and the deprived periphery are two 'transition' regions, one 'upward' and the other 'downward'. In international terms, core areas include North America, Europe and Japan

Coriolis force – when air streams are deflected through the rotation of the Earth on its axis. It can be the cause of storms, including hurricanes

corrasion – see *abrasion

corrosion – the breaking down of something slowly, especially by chemical action

cost-benefit analysis – a technique where projected public schemes are evaluated in terms of social outcomes as well as in terms of profit and loss

crop and pasture management – using management techniques to enhance the quantity and quality of forage supply to grazing animals and to improve the productivity of crops

D

debt – a sum of money that somebody owes

deep sea core sample – a cylindrical section of the Earth's crust removed from the ocean floor. The layers in the core sample tell us about the geologic history of the area

deforestation – the complete clearance of forests by cutting and/or burning

delta – a low-lying area found at the mouth of a river and formed of deposits of alluvium

dependency theory – this explains how poorer and less developed nations depend on wealthier nations for their trade and income

deprivation – lacking in the provision of desired objects or aims

deprivation, index of multiple – used by the UK government as a way of measuring deprivation using six 'domains': health, employment, income, education, the living environment, and barriers to housing and services

destination tourism – when people visit a place simply because of a single attraction, such as the Eden Project in Cornwall or the Great Wall in China

destructive waves – a plunging wave with a short wavelength, high frequency and high crest which breaks so that the wave crashes downwards and erodes the beach

destructive plate boundary – where two *tectonic plates meet and where the denser plate is being destroyed by diving under the less dense plate and being converted to *magma

developed – used to describe a country which has many industries and a complicated economic system

developing – used to describe a country which is poor and trying to make its industry and economic system more advanced

digital divide – the gap between those with regular, effective access to digital and information technology, and those without it

disaster – when a natural hazard has serious effects such as a large loss of life or property

discharge – the quantity of water flowing through any cross-section of a stream or river in unit time

diversify – to spread industrial commitment over a large range of activities so that there is no overdependence on one activity alone

downsizing – a) reducing the number of people who work in a business in order to reduce costs, b) selling your house and moving to a cheaper one in order to save money

drought – a long continuous period of dry weather, caused in Britain by the persistence of warm anticyclones and in the tropics by the failure of the Inter-tropical convergence zone (ITCZ) to move sufficiently far from the equator

dynamic system – a social or geophysical structure that is constantly changing

E

eco-approaches – environmentally friendly ways of addressing a problem

economic migrants – people from a poor area who move to a richer area in search of a better life

edge cities – cities which have grown up on the periphery of older cities, to which new industries and services have moved, away from the old CBD

enclosed or semi-enclosed sea – a gulf, basin or sea connected to another sea or the ocean by a narrow outlet

eustatic changes – a world-wide change of sea level which may be caused by the growth and decay of ice sheets

eutrophic fertile, productive – eutrophication is the process by which ecosystems become more fertile environments as detergents, sewage and artificial fertilizers flow in

exception policy – building on land where it would not normally be permitted, in rural villages where housing needs have been proven

expansion of suburbs and villages – increasing job opportunities in cities lead to people looking for affordable and pleasant housing in settlements within commuter access of the city

exponential – a rate of increase which becomes faster and faster

eye – the calm area at the centre of a hurricane or tropical cyclone

F

fair trade – an organized social and economic movement with regard to trade between developed and developing countries which promotes the payment of a fair price and higher social and environmental standards in areas related to the production of a wide variety of goods

fault line – a fractured surface in the Earth's crust where rocks have travelled relative to each other

fetch – the distance that a sea wave has travelled from its beginning to the coast where it breaks

First World – Western Europe, Japan, Australasia and North America. These were the first areas to industrialise. Also known as the '*developed world'

fjord – a long narrow arm of the sea which is the result of the 'drowning' of a glaciated valley

footloose – industry that can be sited in any of a number of places, often because transport costs are unimportant

formal economy – all kinds of employment which offer regular wages and hours and which carry with them employment rights on which income tax is paid

Fortress Europe – the term sometimes given to the concept of the EU's efforts to keep non-EU goods, businesses and nationals out of the Union's twenty-seven member states

free trade – trade between countries which takes place completely free of restrictions

freeze-thaw – the weathering of rocks which occurs when water which has penetrated joints and cracks freezes and expands

front – the border zone between two air masses which contrast, usually in temperature

fuelwood – wood that is used to produce heat or power. It is normally used in the absence of more efficient fuel sources by poor communities and often involves chopping down scarce tree reserves

G

geology – the scientific study of the Earth, including the origin and history of the rocks and soils of which the Earth is made

geomorphological – to do with the nature and history of landforms and the processes which create them

glaciologist – a scientist who studies glaciers

global conveyor belt – another term for the thermolhaline circulation

greenfield sites – sites which have never been developed or used for an urban use, or are on land that has been brought into active or beneficial use for agriculture or forestry, i.e. fully restored derelict land

greenhouse effect – the warming of the atmosphere as some of its gases absorb the heat given out by the Earth.

grey pound – a term used in the UK to refer to the economic power of older, retired people

greying – a term used to mean the increase in the proportion of older people in a population

H

hazard – an unexpected threat to humans and/or their property. By this definition the Indian monsoon is not a hazard but its failure is

Heavily Indebted Poor Nations (HIPC) – a group of 37 least developed countries with the highest levels of poverty and debt, which are eligible for special assistance from the International Monetary Fund and the *World Bank

hydraulic action – the force of the water within a stream or river

hydrograph – a graph of *discharge or of the level of water in a river over a period of time

I

illegal migrant – an illegal migrant is a foreigner who either has illegally crossed an international political border, be it by land, sea, or air, or a foreigner who has entered a country legally but then overstays his/her visa in order to live and/or work in the country

image – the impression that is given to the public

immigration – the inward flow of people into a country

index of deprivation – see *deprivation

industrial development – the growth of manufacturing industry in an area

informal economy – employment which is not formally recognised. Workers in the informal economy generally do not have contracts, fixed hours or employment benefits

infrastructure – the framework of communication networks, health centres, administration, and power supply necessary for economic development

inner-city zone of transition – according to concentric zone theory this is the crowded , multi-occupied zone of a city first invaded by migrants

inputs – something that is put into a system or project

intangible costs and benefits – costs and benefits that cannot be measured but which are important, such the good and bad effects of a project on people

integrated coastal management – an approach which sees the coastal zone as an interactive and dynamic complex of sub–systems. Human activities in one sub–system may adversely affect other sub-systems. For this reason, it considers that various parts of the coastal zone cannot be considered in isolation

Intergovernmental Panel on Climate Change (IPCC) – a United Nations organization which looks at the evidence and publishes reports on the human impact on climate change

isostatic changes – the rise or fall of the Earth's continental crust, often in response to the melting or accumulation of glacial ice

K

key players – the most important people or organizations involved in a project

L

lag time – the interval between an event and the time when its effects are apparent

lahar – a flow of volcanic debris, either dry or mixed with water as a mud flow

landfill – a site for the disposal of waste materials by burial

legacy – a situation that will exist in the future because of events and actions that take place in the present

longshore drift – the movement of sand and shingle along the coast

low pressure area – another term for a depression

M

magma – the molten rock found below the Earth's surface which can give rise to igneous rocks

magma chamber – a large underground pool of molten rock lying under the surface of the Earth's crust.

manufacturing industry – the mechanized and usually large-scale processing of materials into finished or partly finished products

market-led regeneration – the encouragement of private investment through planning, transport and land policies as well as substantial public investment

mega-delta – where the mouths of several large rivers emerge close together, e.g. the Bay of Bengal

Milankovitch cycles – three interacting astronomical cycles in the Earth's orbit around the Sun, believed to affect long-term climatic change

Millennium Development Goals – eight goals that 192 United Nations member states have agreed to try to achieve by the year 2015 to help raise development standards

minority group – a subordinate group whose members have significantly less control or power over their lives than members of a dominant or majority group

mitigate – to make something less harmful or serious

multiple hazards – where a region suffers from a number of different natural or man-made *hazards, such as unusual tropical storms, tsunamis and rising sea levels, which make life difficult for people living there

N

North Atlantic Drift – a warm ocean current, driven by prevailing south-westerly winds from Florida to north-west Europe, bringing warmer conditions than would otherwise be expected at those latitudes

O

occluded front – where a *cold front catches up with a leading *warm front and lifts it up or where a warm front catches up with a leading cold front and slides over it

OPEC (Organization of the Petroleum Exporting Countries) – an international organisation of oil producing countries which is concerned with the best means of safeguarding their interests, individually and collectively

output – something that comes out of a system

P

pandemic – a disease that spreads over a whole country or across the whole world

periphery – the area most remote from the wealthy 'core' of a country or region

permafrost – areas of rock and soil where temperatures have been below freezing point for at least two years. Permafrost does not have to contain ice

plant succession – the gradual evolution of a series of plants within a given area. This series of plant communities occurs in a roughly predictable order

positive ice albedo effect – when melting snow exposes more dark ground of lower albedo which in turn causes more snow to melt

positive multiplier effect – the positive economic or environmental consequences of an action, e.g. If new jobs are created, people then have money to spend in the shops, which means that more shop workers are needed. The shop workers pay their taxes and spend their new-found money, creating yet more jobs in industries

poverty trap – when people are discouraged from taking higher paid work because that would mean that they would lose their benefit payments. Once income tax and other deductions have been allowed for they would end up earning less

primate city – the largest city within a nation, being more than twice as large as the second city. A primate city dominates the country not only in size but also in influence

privatisation – where government-owned businesses are sold to private owners

push factor – in migration, any adverse factor which causes movement away from the place of residence

pyroclastic flows – a dense cloud of lava fragments thrown out by an erupting volcano as result of bursting gas bubbles within the magma

Q

quotas – a fixed level indicating the maximum amount of imported goods or persons which a state will allow in

R

radiation – energy travelling in the form of electromagnetic waves

re-grading – changing the shape of the landscape by moving soil in large quantities or by shaping cliffs

relief – the shape of the Earth's surface. An area of 'high relief' has large differences in the height of the land; 'low relief' indicates little difference in altitude

remittance payments – money that is sent home to families by people working in a foreign country or in a city in their own country

replacement level – the fertility rate needed to maintain population at its existing size by natural change (without allowing for net immigration)

replacement migration – where migrant workers are encouraged to move from states which have a labour surplus to states which have labour or skills shortages. This requires cooperation between states and is best managed within an organisation like the EU

resource-based industries – these include agriculture, energy, forestry, fisheries, recreation, and mining

reverse colonialism – where companies from previously colonised countries buy up companies in previously colonial countries e.g. Tata Steel from India taking over the British/Dutch steel company Corus in 2006

ripple effect – the effect on house prices as waves of people move from the city to the countryside

rip-rap (also known as revetment, shot rock or rock armour) – rock or other material used to protect shorelines from water erosion

rising limb – that section of a river *hydrograph which covers the beginning of the increased discharge until the maximum flow

rock armour – see *rip-rap

rural housing enabler – a local government officer in the UK dedicated to helping solve the need for affordable housing in rural communities

rurality – the degree to which an area is rural. Rurality can be measured using the Cloke index which employs a number of indicators of rural life

rural-urban migration – the movement of people from the countryside to the cities in search of work

S

sailing and leisure craft – dinghies, yachts and motorboats

saline – salty

salt marsh – mud flats in estuaries and sheltered bays on which vegetation has grown

scenario – a description of how things might happen in the future

scour – to make a passage, hole or mark in the ground or on rocks as a result of movement

sea change – an Australian term for *coastalisation, with the added special sense of people moving to small coastal towns for the improved lifestyle and low house prices

sea floor (or seabed) – the bottom of the ocean

Seasonal Agricultural Workers Scheme (SAWS) – an EU scheme allowing people (mostly students from eastern European countries) to work in other EU countries for limited periods

seasonal workers – a worker who is allowed into a country to work only for a limited period, usually in agriculture

sediment cells – a length of coastline and its associated nearshore area within which the movement of coarse sediment (sand and shingle) is largely self contained. There are 11 sediment cells around England and Wales some of which can be divided into sub-cells

sediment input – the amount of sediment being deposited

service industry – economic activity concerned with the distribution and consumption of goods and services

sewage disposal – the disposal of human excreta and other waterborne waste products from houses, streets, and factories

shanty towns – an area in or near a town where poor people live in houses made of wood, metal or cardboard, often without access to electricity or running water

sheltered accommodation – a term used for self-contained homes specially designed for the elderly. The aim is to provide independent secure accommodation with additional social and domestic facilities

shoreline management plans – plans that take into consideration an entire *sediment cell or sub-cell

slumping – a mass movement where rock and soil move downwards along a concave face

social cohesion – the linking together of people who are tied by one or more specific types of interdependency, such as values, visions, financial ties, friendship and kinship

social exclusion – what can happen when people or areas suffer from a combination of linked problems such as unemployment, poor skills, low incomes, poor housing, high crime, bad health and family breakdown

social landlord – a local authority or a housing association which provides affordable housing to lower income earners on a not-for-profit basis

social segregation – segregation on the basis of class or economic status in which an underclass develops which is separated from the rest of the population

spatial distribution – the spread of varying observations (such as income) within a population across an area

structural adjustment – introducing changes to a nation's economy, such as currency devaluation, promotion of exports and cuts in public services. These changes are usually made in order to qualify for a loan from the IMF

subduction – the transformation into *magma as a dense *tectonic plate dives under a less dense plate at a *destructive plate boundary

subsidy – money that is paid by a government or organization to reduce costs so that prices can be kept low

sustainability – meeting the needs of the present generation without compromising the ability of future generations to fulfil their own needs

swell – a long series of ocean waves, generally produced by wind, and lasting after the wind has ceased

T

tangible costs and benefits – costs and benefits that can be measured, such as things that cost and earn money

tariffs – a list of duties or customs to be paid on imports

tectonic – to do with the processes acting to shape the Earth's crust

tectonic plate – a rigid segment of the Earth's crust which can 'float' across the heavier, semi-molten rock below

terminal groyne syndrome – beach erosion occurring just after the last of a series of groynes

Third World – an outdated term for the poor or developing countries of Africa, Asia, and Latin America

three Ds – jobs which are difficult, dirty and dangerous

topography – the physical features of an area of land, especially the position of its rivers and mountains

Total Fertility Rate (TFR) – the average number of children who would be born per woman if she were to live to the end of her childbearing years and follow normal patterns of fertility

tourist enclave – an area set aside for tourists where they have little or no contact with the society they are visiting. It may have no benefit for the local economy as all its goods and services are brought in from outside

trade winds – tropical easterly winds blowing towards the equator from the subtropical anticyclones at a fairly constant speed

tree line – the line beyond which trees will not grow

tundra – the barren plains of northern Canada, Alaska and Siberia where both temperature and rainfall are low

U

undeveloped – a country which does not have modern industries and has a low standard of living

urban shadow – the effect on a settlement of being close to a city where residents will often commute to the city, turning it into a dormitory settlement

V

vent – the opening in the crust through which volcanic material flows

volcanic emissions – the materials given out when a volcano erupts. These include gas (mainly sulfur dioxide), lava and ash

vulnerable – weak and easily hurt

W

warm front – a *front where the warm air rises over the cold air

World Bank – a bank that is effectively controlled by subscriptions from rich countries which provides aid to the developing world